GEMSTONE
BUYING GUIDE

How to evaluate, identify, select & care for colored gems

Third Edition

Renée Newman

International Jewelry Publications
Los Angeles

Copyright © 2016 by **International Jewelry Publications**
First published 1998
Reprinted 1998
Reprinted 1999
Reprinted 2001
Second Edition 2003
Reprinted 2004
Reprinted 2005
Revised 2005
Reprinted 2006
Revised 2007
Reprinted 2007
Revised 2008
Revised 2010
Revised 2012
Third Edition 2016

All rights reserved. No part of this book may be used, reproduced, or transmitted in any manner whatsoever without written permission from the publisher except in the case of brief quotations used in critical reviews and articles.
    This publication is designed to provide information in regard to the subject matter covered. It is sold with the understanding that the publisher and author are not engaged in rendering legal, financial, or other professional services. If legal or other expert assistance is required, the services of a competent professional should be sought. International Jewelry Publications and the author shall have neither liability nor responsibility to any person or entity with respect to any loss or damage caused or alleged to be caused directly or indirectly by the information contained in this book. All inquiries should be directed to:

International Jewelry Publications
P.O. Box 13384
Los Angeles, CA 90013-0384 USA

(Inquiries should be accompanied by a self-addressed, stamped envelope.)

Printed in the U.S.A.

Library of Congress Cataloging-in-Publication Data

Names: Newman, Renée - author.
Title: Gemstone buying guide : how to evaluate, identify, select & care for
    colored gems / Renée Newman.
Description: Third edition. | Los Angeles : International Jewelry
    Publications, 2016. | Includes bibliographical references and index.
Identifiers: LCCN 2016001541 | ISBN 9780929975511 (pbk.)
Subjects: LCSH: Precious stones--Purchasing.
Classification: LCC TS752 .N49 2016 | DDC 553.8068/7--dc23
LC record available at http://lccn.loc.gov/2016001541

Front cover photo: Colored gemstone suite from Cynthia Renée Inc; photo: Robert Weldon. Starting in the front, left to right: first row: pink oval: unheated Burma hot pink sapphire, light green cushion: grossular garnet, orange freeform: Mexican fire opal
2nd row: Blue round: tanzanite, orange trillion: Oregon sunstone from Oregon, blue oval: sapphire, yellow cushion: danburite
3rd row: green round: Burmese peridot, light blue cushion square: blue topaz, ametrine
back row: red tourmaline

Spine photo: Chrysoprase, fire opal & danburite earring by Cynthia Renée; photo: Robert Weldon.

Back cover photo: Purple spinel, sphene & tourmaline cut and photographed by Jeff White.

Contents

Acknowledgments

I would like to express my appreciation to the following people for their contribution to the *Gemstone Buying Guide*:

Ernie and Regina Goldberger of the Josam Diamond Trading Corporation. This book could never have been written without the experience and knowledge I gained from working with them.

Eve Alfillé, Arthur Anderson, Kurt Baker, Charles Carmona, Clint Cross, Paul Cory, Michael Cowing, Dr. Paul Downing, Pete Flusser, Si and Ann Frazier, Mark Gronlund, Cary Harris, Don Kay, Dr. Horst Krupp, Glenn Lehrer, Gail Levine, Peter Malnekoff, Cynthia Marcusson, Dr. Kurt Nassau, Pierre Paré, Howard Rubin, Sindi Schloss, Sherris Cottier Shank, Gerald Stockton, John S. White and Larry Woods. They have made valuable suggestions, corrections and comments regarding the portions of the book they examined. They are not responsible for any possible errors, nor do they necessarily endorse the material contained in this book.

Clint Cross, Pete & Bobbi Flusser, Carrie Ginsburg Fine Gems, Mark Gronlund, Josam Diamond Trading Corporation, Danny & Ronny Levy Fine Gems, Louisa McKay, Overland Gems, Inc, Andrew Sarosi, Gerald Stockton, Timeless Gem Designs. Their stones or jewelry have been used for some of the photographs.

Gordon Aatlo, Jack Abraham, Advanced Quality Co. Ltd. Eve J. Allfilé, American Gemological Laboratories, Mark Anderson, Nancy Arthur-McGehee, Asian Institute of Gemological Sciences, Auction Market Resource, Peter Barr, Bear Essentials, Jeffery Bergman, Bonhams, George Bosshart, Boston Gems, John Bradshaw, Ashleigh Branstetter, Katy Briscoe, Burtis Blue Turquoise, Loretta Castoro, Emily Chesick, Coast to Coast Rarestones, Skip Colflesh, ColorMasters Gem Corp, Columbia Gem House, Commercial Mineral Company, Hanna Cook Wallace, Peggy Croft, Erica Courtney, William Cox, Paula Crevoshay, Cynthia Renée Inc, Thomas Dailing, Desert Sun Mining & Gems, Different Seasons Jewelry, Division of Minerals and Energy Resources, South Australia, William Thomas Dodge, Jessica Dow, John Dyer, Lisa Elser, Fine Gems International, Fire Agate Art Studio, Gem Testing Laboratory of The Gem and Jewelry Institute of Thailand, Gemological Institute of America, Gary Dulac Goldsmith, Lucas Fassari, Mark Gronlund, Henry A. Hänni, Cary Harris, Barbara Heinrich, Frank Heiser, Hopkins Opal, Hubert Inc, Iteco, Inc., Jade by Nikolai, Catherine & Michael Jensen, Joni-Gems, Jye Luxury Collection, Amy Kahn Russell, Robert Kane, Korite International, Richard Krementz Gemstones, Lang Antiques San Francisco, Catherine Lehman, Glenn Lehrer Designs, Gail Levine, Mark Henry Jewelry, Mason-Kay, Inc, Mayer & Watt, Fred Mouawad, Murphy Design, New Era Gems, Omi Privé, Pala International, Pearce Design, Perlas del Mar de Cortez, Precious Gem Resources, Primagem, Linda Quinn, Rainforest Design, Revelations in Stone, Barbara Westwood, Whitney Robinson, Carina Rossner, Sami's Fine Jewelry, Sapphires of Montana, Sarosi by Timeless Gems, Sindi Schloss, Georg Schmerholz, Mark Schneider, Sherris Cottier Shank, Stephen Vincent Design, Gerald Stockton,

Stone Group Labs, Studio Jewelers, Sugarman-Franz Designs, Suna Bros, Nikolai Tsang, Larry Walker, Dennis Walters, Leslie Weinberg, Emil Weis Opals, Robert & Orasa Weldon, Jeff White, John S. White, Bear & Cara Williams, Deborah Wilson, Larry Woods, Zaffiro, Zava Mastercuts. Photos or diagrams from them have been reproduced in this book.

Frank Chin, Diana Jarrett & Dean Lange. They have provided technical assistance.

Louise Harris Berlin. She has spent hours carefully editing the *Gemstone Buying Guide*. Thanks to her, this book is much easier for consumers to read and understand.

My sincere thanks to all of these contributors for their kindness and help.

1

Price Factors in a Nutshell

The following factors can affect the prices of colored gemstones:

♦ **Color**
♦ **Clarity** (degree to which a stone is free from inclusions and blemishes)
♦ **Transparency**
♦ **Shape**
♦ **Cutting style**
♦ **Cut quality** (proportions and finish)
♦ **Carat weight or stone size**
♦ **Brilliance (Brightness)**
♦ **Treatment status** (untreated or treated? type and extent of the treatment)
♦ **Place of origin** (country, region or mine)
♦ **Copper, chromium and/or vanadium content**
♦ **Distinctness of phenomena** if present (e.g., stars, cat's-eyes, alexandrite's change of color)

Price Factors Explained

COLOR plays a major role in gem pricing, but its impact varies depending on the quality, size, variety and species of a gemstone. (A variety is a category within a gem species; e.g., amethyst and rock crystal are varieties of quartz, which is a species). Color has a greater effect on the price of blue sapphire, for example, than on blue topaz or yellow sapphire. Here are some guidelines:

In most cases, the stronger and more saturated the color, the more it is valued. For example, a strong green emerald can cost many times more than a lighter green emerald all other factors being equal.

In some cases, buyer/seller preferences impact prices more than the strength of the color. The Burma sapphire in figure 1.1 has a stronger blue color than the one from Sri Lanka in figure 1.2, yet some people in the trade would prefer the lighter blue color and consider it just as valuable. Both sapphires are beautiful and the fact that their color is natural and not the result of heat treatment makes them exceptional.

Fig. 1.1 Unheated Burma sapphire.
Sapphire & photo: Fred Mouawad.

Fig. 1.2 Unheated Sri Lankan sapphire.
Sapphire & photo: Fred Mouawad.

Fig. 1.3 Carved leopard skin jasper in a platinum and 18 karat gold butterfly brooch created by Eve J. Alfillé—an example of how an artist can transform an inexpensive brown, beige, and black stone into a museum-quality jewelry piece. *Design © by Eve J, Alfillé: photo by Matthew Arden.*

In most cases, the more grayish, brownish or blackish a gemstone is, the lower its price unless it's supposed to be black or brown. There's agreement in the trade that a blackish or grayish sapphire is far less valuable than a saturated blue one. Nevertheless, just because a stone is brownish or black, does not mean it's undesirable. Consider the jasper butterfly brooch in figure 1.3. Many people would reject a brown and black spotted stone like this one. Yet this is a stunning piece and the brown diamonds are the perfect accent for it.

The more rare a color is, the more it may be valued. In opal, red is the rarest color, so it's the most highly valued. In ammolite, blue is more rare so it's more prized. It's the rarity of the color, not just the color itself, that often determines prices.

Fig. 1.4 Rare black opal with broad flashes of red and other colors. "World of Opals" Los Angeles 11/24/2014 Bonhams auction; photo © Bonhams, all rights reserved.

Fig. 1.5 A high quality black opal with bright blue to green play-of-color accented by sapphires, tsavorites and diamonds. *Ring & photo from Omi Privé.*

In most cases, the lower the quality of a stone, the less impact color has on price. Color has little influence on the price of low-grade translucent to opaque emeralds, but it has a significant effect on top-grade emeralds.

Low price does not necessarily mean low desirability. Light colored, low-priced gems can be quite attractive when well cut.

In many cases, the more uniform the color, the more the stone is valued. Top quality jade cabochons have a uniform color throughout the stone. The more uneven or blotchy the color is, the lower the value. However, jade with multiple colors within the same stone can be very expensive if the colors are intense and distinct.

Color zoning in faceted gems tends to lower stone prices, but in some cases the zoning makes the stone more unique and attractive, thereby increasing its value.

Chapter 4 has more guidelines on evaluating the color of gems and information about the effect of lighting on color. To learn more on how color affects the price of different gem varieties, see Chapter 11.

CLARITY is the degree to which a stone is free from flaws (inclusions and blemishes). Usually, the fewer, smaller and less noticeable the flaws, the higher the price, especially for higher priced gems such as rubies and emeralds. However there's a greater tolerance for inclusions in colored gems than in diamonds, and prices are typically based on the visual appearance of colored stones rather than on clarity grades. There is no universally accepted grading system for colored gems. In some cases, inclusions may be a welcome sign that a stone is natural and not treated nor lab-grown. For more information and photos on clarity, see Chapter 5.

TRANSPARENCY is the degree to which a gem is clear, hazy, translucent or opaque. (An opaque material does not allow light to pass through it; a translucent material resembles frosted glass.) Normally the higher the transparency the more valuable the stone. There are a few exceptions. Rubies and sapphires with microscopic particles that disperse the color may be valued the same or sometimes a bit more than stones with a diamond-like transparency. For black opal, opaque stones tend to be more highly valued than those with a higher transparency.

Transparency can have a major impact on the value of a gemstone, especially for emerald, ruby, sapphire, opal, jade, star gems and cat's-eye gems. For example, a $50 sapphire that's nearly opaque could possibly sell for thousands of dollars if it were transparent. See Chapter 5 for additional information.

Fig. 1.6 Emerald with a high transparency and noticeable inclusions. *Photo © Renée Newman.*

Fig. 1.7 Less transparent emerald than the one in figure 1.6. *Photo © Renée Newman.*

SHAPE is a gem's face-up outline (e.g., round or pear shaped). Color, clarity and transparency normally play a greater role in determining the price of colored gems than shape, cutting style and cut quality. Nevertheless, these latter three factors can affect the value of such stones.

The effect of shape on price varies depending on the seller, the gem variety, the stone weight, the stone quality and the demand for the shape. A *high-quality*, one-carat round ruby, for example, may cost 10% to 20% more than one with an oval shape because of greater demand and because there's more weight loss from the rough when cutting rounds. In small sizes and low qualities, the shape may have no effect on the price. The subject of shape pricing is complex. Simply remember to compare gemstones of the same shape and cutting style when evaluating gem prices.

The symmetry of the shape outline can also affect the per-carat price of large, high quality gems because symmetrical stones are desirable and may require more loss of weight from the rough.

CUTTING STYLE is the way in which a stone is cut or faceted. **Cabochons** (unfaceted dome-shaped stones) and unfaceted beads are generally priced lower than faceted stones because they cost less to cut than faceted styles. Another reason cabochons are usually priced less is that they're often made from lower quality material that is unsuitable for faceting. Cabochon stones can also be of high quality, especially those found in antique jewelry.

Designer and trademarked cutting styles often sell for more than generic cuts of the same shape. The percentage impact tends to be the greatest for lower priced stones such as amethyst and blue topaz. A $20 well-cut standard oval blue topaz might sell for $100 if it had a unique faceting style or carved image created by a renowned cutter.

CUT QUALITY refers to the proportions and finish, also called **make**. This is a crucial factor because it affects the brilliance and color of gems, but its importance is not always reflected in the price of colored gems. Two of the main considerations of cut quality are:

1. **Do you see color all across the stone when you look at it face up?** Well-cut stones do not have large black areas nor do they have an obvious **window**—a pale, washed out area in the middle of stones that allows you to see right through them. In general, the larger the window, the poorer the cut. Even color throughout the stone indicates good cut quality.

Fig. 1.8 Ametrine with a window. *Photo © Renée Newman.*

Fig. 1.9 Red beryl with no window. *Cut by John Dyer; photo by Lydia Dyer.*

2. **Are you paying for excess weight?** Suppose you have two stones with the same face-up size that are priced by carat weight. One is well cut and one has an overly deep and fat bottom andweighs twice as much. The overly deep stone would cost twice as much even though it has the same face-up size. In addition, it may be impractical for mounting and appear overly dark.

   Keep in mind, however, that colored gems with good brilliance and color must often be cut deeper than diamonds. If colored stones are cut too shallow, they will have a window. See Chapter 6 for more information and photos on judging cut quality.

CARAT WEIGHT OR STONE SIZE is also an important value factor. In most cases, the higher the carat-weight category, the greater the per-carat price of a gem. A carat is a unit of weight equaling 1/5 of a gram.

Many translucent to semiopaque stones such as jade, malachite and chalcedony are usually sold by the piece or stone size, not by weight. Designer cuts may also be priced per piece, and colored stones under approximately half a carat are often priced according to millimeter size. Chapter 3 has additional information on carat weight.

BRILLIANCE (BRIGHTNESS) is the strength and amount of light returned by a gemstone. In stones such as opal, ammolite and fire agate, this is considered a separate value factor. Opal brightness is frequently judged on a scale of 1–5 with 5 being the brightest level. Diamond grading labs often include brilliance as a component of their cut grade. Brightness is one of the most important factors in valuing gems.

TREATMENT STATUS includes three elements which can be important if you're spending a substantial amount of money on a gemstone:

1. **Is the stone treated or untreated?** Has the stone undergone a process other than cleaning, cutting or polishing to improve its natural appearance? Most colored stones are treated in some way by man. High quality untreated gems are usually the most highly valued because they're more rare and they're natural. However, an ugly untreated stone is typically worth less and harder to sell than one that's attractive and treated. That's why gems are treated.

2. **What treatment(s) did the stone undergo?** Not all treatments are equal. Some treatments, such as dyeing and cavity filling, have a more negative impact on value than others, like heat treatment, which is well accepted. Therefore it pays to find out what gem treatments were used on a gem before assessing its value. Chapter 8 discusses the various types of gem treatments.

3. **What is the extent of treatment?** This applies to clarity enhancements such as fracture filling. For example, practically all emeralds have tiny fractures. So it's customary to fill these fractures with an oil, wax or epoxy-type substance to mask them and sometimes increase durability. Assume that all emeralds you see for sale have been clarity enhanced, unless otherwise stated. Naturally a stone with a minor amount of filling is more valued than one with a substantial amount throughout the stone. Therefore gem labs now indicate on their documents the extent of the filling process, often by describing it as minor, moderate, significant, or none.

PLACE OF ORIGIN may refer to the country, area, or mine where a gem was mined. In most cases the source of colored gems does not matter—it's the quality that counts. However, for gems such as ruby, sapphire, emerald and green-blue tourmaline, origin can affect the price, provided the stone has a high quality and is accompanied by a lab report indicating a desired source. For example, good quality sapphires from Kashmir sell at a premium because of their rarity and exceptional color.

DISTINCTNESS OF PHENOMENA: Phenomena are unusual optical effects, e.g.,

♦ **Chatoyancy** (cat's-eye): a band of reflected light in cabochons (gems with a domed, polished surface). It occurs when a strong light strikes needle-like inclusions or hollow tubes that are parallel within the stone. A cat's-eye effect may be seen on some chrysoberyl, emerald, aquamarine, apatite, quartz and tourmaline.

♦ **Asterism** (star): bands of reflected light crossing each other in the center to form a star with four, six or twelve rays. (See Chapter 7 for more information).

♦ **Adularescence**: a floating, shifting light effect caused by structural unevenness in moonstone, which scatters the light. On some high dome moonstones, it creates a cat's-eye effect.

Gem Phenomena

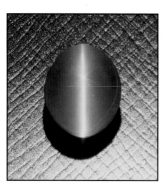

Chatoyancy: Cat's-eye

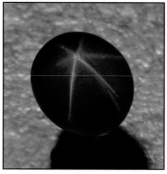

Asterism: Burma star sapphire
Mayer & Watt / Geoffrey Watt

Adularescence: Moonstone
Zaffiro / Elizabeth Gualtieri

Iridescence: Ammolite. *Pendant and photo from Korite Intl.*

Change of Color: Alexandrite. Mayer & Watt / Geoffrey Watt.

Labradorescence: Labradorite

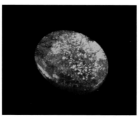

Aventurescence: Sunstone

Play-of-Color: Mintabie opal (70.63 cts). *Bear Essentials / Bear Williams.*

- ♦ **Aventurescence**: a glittery, sparkling effect caused by light reflecting off of minute platelike inclusions. In sunstone, the inclusions are usually platelets of copper or hematite, and in aventurine quartz they're a type of green mica.

- ♦ **Labradorescence**: a flash of color(s) in labradorite or spectrolite seen at certain viewing angles. It's caused by the interference of light through the layered structure of the labradorite.

- ♦ **Color change**: sometimes called the alexandrite effect. A change of color that occurs when the light source is changed. For example, an alexandrite, garnet or sapphire may appear purplish under incandescent light (e.g., light bulb), but green in daylight or fluorescent light.

- ♦ **Orient**: pearl iridescence. It results from the interference that occurs as light passes through layers of nacre. Orient may be a subtle combination of rainbow-like colors or of pink, blue, silver and sometimes green (fig. 1.22).

Iridescent Gems

Fig. 1.18 Fire obsidian. *William Thomas (Tom) Dodge; photo: Jeff Scovil.*

Fig. 1.19 Spectrolite front and back view. *Pendant by Different Seasons Jewelry; photo by Jessica Dow.*

Fig. 1.21 Fire agate. *Gem and photo by Ryszard Krukowski of Fire Agate Art Studio.*

Fig. 1.20 Ammolite. *Necklace and photograph from Korite International.*

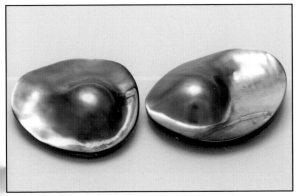

Fig 1.22 Cultured blister pearls from the *Pteria Sterna* oyster. *Pearls and photo from Perlas del Mar de Cortez ®.*

Fig. 1.23 Rainbow iris agate. *Carving and photo by Glenn Lehrer.*

◆ **Iridescence**: a play of lustrous changing colors caused by the interference of light. The GIA (Gemological Institute of America) uses it to refer to the color phenomena of gems such as fire agate, rainbow agate and ammolite. Rainbow hematite also qualifies.

"Iridescence" has different meanings to different trade members. Some feel that a gem must show all colors of the rainbow to be classified iridescent; others require at last three colors, and still others would classify a solid red ammolite as iridescent as long as the quality of the color changes when the stone is moved. Some people extend the meaning of "iridescence" to describe the phenomena of gems such as labradorite and opal.

Trade members generally agree that the spectral (rainbow-like) effects seen in diamonds and demantoid garnet should be called "dispersion" or "fire" not iridescence. There seems to be agreement, too, that iridescent colors must have a shifting quality rather than a static, fixed position like you'll see in banded agate or watermelon tourmaline (color zoning).

Occasionally, the term "iridescent" is applied to gems with fractures displaying rainbow colors like those in the barite of figure 1.24. However, stones like these are not considered to be "phenomenal gems" by appraisers, nor do gem texts list such gems as iridescent gem species.

Fig. 1.24 Natural iridescence along a barite fracture ("feather"). *Photo by Lucas Fassari.*

◆ **Play-of-color**: a display of shifting colors in opal that is caused by the interaction of light with clusters of microscopic silica spheres of uniform size, which break up the light into spectral colors. The term "play-of-color" specifically applies to the flashing colors of opal, not to the iridescence in other gems.

Fig. 1.25 Play-of-color in Lightning Ridge black opal. *Ring by Mark Anderson of Different Seasons Jewelry; photo by Jessica Dow.*

In general, the sharper and more obvious the phenomena, the more valuable the stone, all other factors being equal. However, don't expect the phenomena of natural stones to be as distinct as those on man-made stones. For example, the sharper and more noticeable a star, the more valuable the stone, unless it's a synthetic star. Natural stars are generally not as perfect as those on man-made stones.

COPPER, CHROMIUM AND/OR VANADIUM CONTENT can affect the prices of some tourmaline. Blue to green tourmaline gems with lab reports stating that they are colored primarily by copper can sell for several thousand dollars per carat depending on their size and quality. They are called cuprian tourmalines or copper-bearing tourmalines.

Tourmaline that is colored by chromium and/or vanadium is called chrome tourmaline by the GIA and World Jewellery Confederation (CIBJO). It is generally priced significantly higher than most other green tourmaline that is not colored by copper, chromium, and/or vanadium. One exception is some of the medium green tourmalines mined in Afghanistan. In sizes above five carats they look brighter and therefore more attractive than chrome tourmaline. Consequently these non-chrome tourmalines may sometimes command comparable or even higher prices.

Two Common Beliefs Which Warrant Review

1. **Color is just a matter of individual preference.** This is a common answer to the question, "What is the most valuable color?" The erroneous implication is that there are no trade standards for preferred colors. The pricing of colored gems is based on some universal principles regarding gem color—normally the less brown or gray present and the more saturated the color, the more valuable the stone. There are some exceptions. As already mentioned, the preferred strength of the blue in sapphires may vary depending on the nationality of the buyer.

   For each gemstone, there is also a range of hues which command a higher price than others. Often, the closer gems are to a pure red, green or blue, the more valued their color is. Again there are exceptions, as is the case with greenish blue Paraiba tourmaline, which can wholesale for more than thirty thousand dollars per carat because of its rarity.

   Even though your choice of color should be determined by what you like, you need to know how color is valued in order to accurately compare prices.

2. **Color is the most important factor for valuing colored stones**. Color is a major value factor, but it's not always the most important one. Suppose you have a fine $100,000 jade cabochon. If it were semiopaque with the same color, it would be worth a fraction of that amount. If the jade had been acid treated and filled with a polymer, it could be worth less than $500. Transparency and treatment status can sometimes be more important than color when valuing gems.

   Fractures in tanzanite have a significant effect both on its price and salability. On the other hand, light purple colors can be quite desirable even though they're priced lower than deep blues. If you examined the reject stones of colored-stone dealers, you'd find that most were rejected because of poor clarity and/or transparency. This doesn't mean clarity is more important than color; it just indicates that the importance of each grading factor varies from one stone to another. Consumers who focus on color and play down other value factors risk getting a poor buy. **When buying colored gems, remember—color is not everything,** even though it does play a substantial role. **Other factors can be equally important.**

Colored Gem Pricing

Some consumers think that dealers evaluate colored gems in a logical, analytical manner. Unlike diamond dealers, colored-gem dealers do not assign color and clarity grades according to a standardized grading system, nor do they list proportion measurements such as the angle of the top of the stone (crown angle).

Colored-gem dealers tend to evaluate gem quality as a whole rather than breaking it down to its constituent parts of color, clarity, transparency, proportions, etc. Their final judgments are usually more intuitive than logical.

Non-quality-related factors also enter into their pricing strategies. Some of these price determinants are demand, form of payment, buyer's credit rating, amount purchased, competitors' prices. time of sale, the customer's eagerness to buy, the seller's need for money and his assessment of the buyer. Astute, knowledgeable buyers tend to be offered better prices.

Since you can't always count on prices to reflect the quality of gems, it's all the more important that you learn to make quality judgments yourself. The reason this book analyzes color and gem quality in terms of their component parts is to aid you in this process. Vague statements such as "look for color" are not helpful to consumers. However, when you learn how color and other price factors affect the cost of a gem, it's easier for you to understand gem valuation. Your ultimate goal should be to reach the level where you can make quick comprehensive judgments about gem quality, as a dealer would. But like any other skill, this takes practice.

Independent gem lab documents and appraisals are recommended for verifying the identity, origin and treatment status of gemstones, especially for major purchases. Even experienced dealers realize the need for assistance from reputable gem labs when buying and selling gems. Consult the *Gem & Jewelry Pocket Guide* by Renée Newman for sample lab documents and information on choosing appraisers and gem labs,

Chapter 11 gives some broad price ranges for many of the gem varieties that are listed. Keep in mind that colored gem prices can change rapidly because of world events, new finds or mine closings. For example, the price of green-blue tourmaline from Paraiba, Brazil has skyrocketed because of high demand and lack of availability.

For most gems, the price ranges are broad because of the variability in the quality. You can find very low-grade one-carat emeralds at public gem shows retailing for as low as $10. On the other hand, you can find top-grade one-carat emeralds retailing for as much as $15,000. In addition, within a given emerald quality type, there's a lot of price variation because of the numerous suppliers and geographic sources of emerald. Consequently it's impossible to indicate specific prices for emeralds. Keep in mind that a $1000 one-carat emerald, for example, may be a better buy than a $100 one-carat emerald. You must consider its quality and treatment status.

It's easier to be more specific about a gem such as benitoite, a transparent blue gemstone mined in California. There's only one distributer of faceted benitoite.

Use the price ranges in this book only as a general guideline of the relative values of gems. They may be obsolete when you read them, so do your own comparison shopping, and deal with knowledgeable sellers who will look after your interests. Don't become so focused on price that you overlook aesthetic features. Gems do not have to be of top quality to be acceptable, but they should meet *your* needs in terms of beauty and pizazz.

2

Shape & Cutting Style

When gemologists speak of a gem's **shape**, they usually mean its face-up outline. The most common gemstone shapes include the round, oval, square, triangle, pear, marquise, heart and **cushion**, a squarish or rectangular shape with curved sides and rounded corners. Gems can be any geometric shape or they may resemble things such as animals, bells, stars, the moon, etc. They can also be cut as abstract freeforms. Gem cutters try to select shapes and cutting styles which allow them to emphasize preferred colors and brilliance, minimize undesirable flaws, and/or get the maximum weight yield from the rough. In small calibrated sizes, there is a tendency to cut what jewelry manufacturers want, even when some shapes cause a greater weight loss. Standard sizes and shapes are required for mass-produced jewelry.

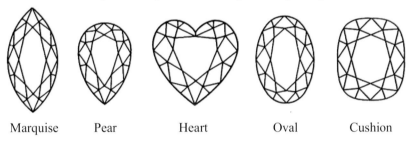

| Marquise | Pear | Heart | Oval | Cushion |

Cutting style refers to the way in which a stone is cut or faceted. An oval-shaped stone, for example, may just be rounded as a cabochon or it may have facets (polished surfaces with varying shapes) that are arranged in different styles. The term **emerald cut** has a double meaning. It indicates that the shape is square or rectangular with beveled (slanted) corners and that the faceting style is a step cut, which has parallel rows of long, four-sided facets. A **radiant cut** has the same shape as an emerald cut but has facets similar to those of a round brilliant cut.

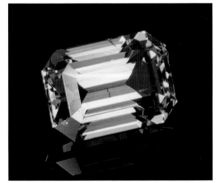

Fig. 2.2 Emerald cut Mali garnet. *Cut and photographed by Clay Zava.*

Fig. 2.3 Radiant cut garnet from the Umba Valley of Tanzania. *Cut and photographed by Clay Zava of Zava Mastercuts.*

Sometimes rough gem material is not cut into any particular shape. Instead, it is just rounded and polished leaving the basic shape of the rough intact. This process is called **tumbling** and is generally used when the material doesn't warrant cutting. The rough pieces are tumbled in a rotating barrel with abrasives and water. As the stones slide against each other, they become smooth like pebbles in rivers that rub against sand and other pebbles. Tumbling is the simplest technique for fashioning gem rough. The resulting shape is described as **baroque**, which means "irregular in outline."

Fig. 2.4 Tumbled Oregon sunstone. *Beads & photo from Desert Sun Mining & Gems.*

Gemstone Terms Defined

To help you understand the sections on cutting styles, here are some basic terms:

Facets: The polished surfaces or planes on a stone. Normally they're flat, but some cutters are now creating stones with concave facets. Facets are intended to create brilliance in a gemstone.

Table: The large, flat top facet. It normally has an octagonal shape on a round stone.

Girdle: The narrow rim around the stone. The girdle plane is parallel to the table and is the largest diameter of any part of the stone.

Crown: The upper part of the stone above the girdle.

Pavilion: The lower part of the stone below the girdle.

Culet: The tiny facet on the pointed bottom of the pavilion, parallel to the table. Sometimes the point of a stone is called "the culet" even if no culet facet is present.

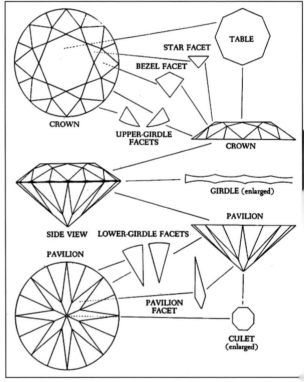

Fig. 2.5 Facet arrangement of a round brilliant cut. *Diagram reprinted with permission from Gemological Institute of America*

Fancy Shape: Any shape except round. This term is most frequently applied to diamonds.

Rough: Gem material in its natural state as it comes out of the ground prior to cutting or polishing.

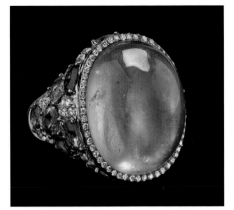

Fig. 2.6 Aquamarine cabochon (28.12 cts). *Ring by Hubert; photo by Diamond Graphics.*

Fig. 2.7 Sugarloaf emerald cabochon (15.26 cts). *Ring by Hubert Inc; photo by Diamond Graphics.*

Traditional Cutting Styles

Before the 1300's, gems were usually cut into unfaceted rounded beads or into cabochons (unfaceted dome-shaped stones). Colored gems looked attractive cut this way, but diamonds looked dull. Thanks to man's interest in bringing out the beauty of diamonds, the art of faceting gemstones was developed. At first, facets were added haphazardly, but by around 1450, diamonds began to be cut with a symmetri-

Fig. 2.8 Table cut

cal arrangement of facets. The first symmetrical style probably evolved out of the natural octahedral shape of some diamond crystals. Simply by flattening one point or cutting it off, a table facet was formed. This created a symmetrical style called the **table cut**, which had a crown, pavilion and nine facets (ten if there were a culet). More complex styles gradually emerged, and there were advances in cutting tools and technology. One of the most important developments was the introduction of the rotary diamond saw around 1900. By the 1920's, the modern round-brilliant cut had become popular.

As cutters discovered how faceting could bring out the brilliance and sparkle of diamonds, they started to apply the same techniques to colored stones. Today, gems are cut into the following basic styles:

CABOCHON CUT: Has a dome-shaped top and either a flat or rounded bottom. This is the simplest cut for a stone and is often seen in antique jewelry. In today's fashion world, this type of cut has become more popular for colored gemstones; it is always used for star and cat's-eye gems. Sometimes stones are cut as a cabochon on top and faceted on the bottom to add some brilliance. When a cabochon has a square, rectangular or triangular base with rounded edges that taper to a point, it's called a **sugarloaf cabochon**.

Cabochon

Since the **cabochon** is the simplest style, it costs less to cut than faceted styles. Another reason cabochons are generally priced less is that they are often made from lower quality material that is unsuitable for faceting. Cabochon stones can also be cut from high quality transparent gem material, especially those found in antique jewelry.

Fig. 2.10 Emerald-cut tanzanite (38.51 cts). *Pendant: Hubert; photo: Diamond Graphics.*

Fig. 2.11 Round brilliant cut pink sapphire. *Ring by Hubert; photo: Diamond Graphics.*

STEP CUT: Has rows of facets that resemble the steps of a staircase. The facets are usually four-sided and elongated, and parallel to the girdle. One example is the **baguette**, a square-cornered, rectangular stone. If step-cuts have clipped-off corners, they're called **emerald cuts** because emeralds are often cut this way. This protects the corners and provides places where prongs can secure the stone. Emerald cuts are usually rectangular or square, but they can also be triangular. They tend to have more facets than baguettes. Light-colored emerald cuts often have more facets than shown in figure 2.10 below. The additional facets help maximize brilliance.

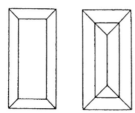

Fig 2.12 Step-cut baguette

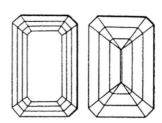

Fig. 2.13 Emerald cut

BRILLIANT CUT: Has mostly 3-sided facets which radiate outward from the stone. Kite- or lozenge-shaped facets may also be present. The best-known example is the **full-cut round brilliant**, which has 58 facets. Ovals, pears, marquises, and heart-shapes can also be brilliant-cut. The **single cut**, which has 17 or 18 facets, is another type of brilliant cut. It may be found on

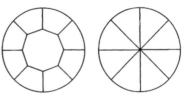

Fig. 2.14 Single cut

small stones, often of low quality, or on imitations. Square stones cut in the brilliant style are called **princess cuts**. Triangular brilliant cuts are called **trilliants**. The princess and trilliant cuts were originally developed for diamonds because their brilliant-style facets create a greater amount of brilliance and sparkle than step facets do. Now the princess and trilliant cuts are becoming popular for colored stones.

Fig. 2.15 Mixed-cut spinel (10.27 cts) from the Mahenge area of Tanzania. *Spinel from Pala International; photo by Mia Dixon.*

Fig. 2.16 Trilliant-cut citrine from the Madeira basin in Brazil. *Cut & photographed by Clay Zava of Zava Mastercuts.*

Gemstone pendants or earrings are occasionally cut as **briolettes**. These have a tear-drop shape, a circular cross-section and brilliant-style facets (or occasionally rectangular, step-cut-style facets or else no facets).

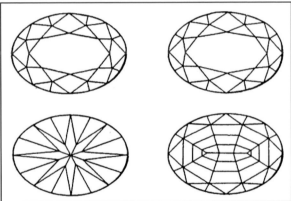

Fig. 2.17 Prasiolite (green quartz) briolette. *Pendant by Hubert; photo by Diamond Graphics.*

Fig. 2.18 Brilliant cut

Fig. 2.19 Mixed cut

MIXED CUT: Has both step- and brilliant-cut facets. This is a popular faceting style for colored stones. The crown is brilliant-cut to maximize brilliance and hide flaws if present. The pavilion, on the other hand, is either entirely step cut or else has a combination of both step- and brilliant-type facets. The step facets allow cutters to save weight and bring out the color of the stone. Occasionally, the mixed cut is referred to as the **Ceylon cut**.

BEAD (FACETED & UNFACETED): Usually has a ball-shaped form with a hole through the center. Most faceted beads have either brilliant- or step-type facets. Today, beads are generally made from lower-priced material. High-quality rubies and emeralds, for example, are usually faceted. It would be pointless to lower their weight and value by drilling holes through them. On the other hand, high quality material is often used for jade beads.

Non-traditional Cuts

Many people use the term **fancy cut** to refer to almost any cut which is not a standard cabochon, brilliant-cut or step cut. One example is the **bufftop**, a gem that's faceted underneath with a cabochon top. Traditional step- and brilliant-cut stones have a large table facet on the crown.

Fig. 2.20 Bufftop

Contemporary cutters sometimes eliminate the table. They may facet squares or rectangles of similar size across the crown. This is called a **checkerboard cut** or **opposed-bar cut**, depending on the style. Another example of a faceting style without a table is the old-style **rose cut**, which has brilliant-style facets, a dome-shaped crown, a flat base and a round girdle outline. The **rose cut** may have originated in India and probably dates back to the fifteenth century. Rose cuts may also be cut with a pavilion.

Traditionally, the facets on gems have been flat. In recent years, some gem cutters have been experimenting with **concave facets.** By using concave shapes, faceters can create scalloped girdle outlines and increase brilliance. If light enters a gem and hits a flat facet, it is reflected in one direction.

Fig. 2.21 Rose cut

However, if it hits a curved surface, it is scattered in many directions, thereby magnifying the brilliance of the stone. Concave faceting normally takes about two to five times longer than conventional faceting. Consequently, stones with concave facets usually cost more than traditional cuts.

Fig. 2.22 Half-barrel shaped rubellite with a checkerboard faceting style. *Ring by Gary Dulac; photo by Azad.*

Fig. 2.23 Concave faceted amethyst cut by Mark Gronlund. *Photo © R. Newman.*

An **open table** is a concept that eliminates the crown and spreads the table so that the observer's eye is drawn into the interior of the stone. Both curved and flat facets may be used on the pavilion to create unusual patterns and optical effects when the stone is viewed face up. Sometimes the entire center of the stone is cut out and there is neither a table nor a pavilion.

The term **designer cut** is used to describe unusual faceting styles and face-up patterns created with traditional faceting methods. Figures 2.24–2.29 are examples.

Fig. 2.24 Montana sapphire (1.93 cts) StarBrite™. *Cut by John Dyer & Co; photo by Priscilla Dyer.*

Fig. 2.25 Untreated Oregon sunstone (5.13 cts) StarBrite™. *Cut by John D. Dyer & Co; photo by Priscilla Dyer.*

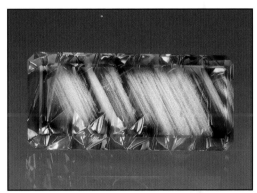

Fig. 2.26 Citrine (24.45 ct). *Cut by Lisa Elser; photo by C. Tom Schlegel.*

Fig. 2.27 Untreated Oregon sunstone (16.58 cts) ZigZag™ cut. *Cut by John D. Dyer & Co; photo by Priscilla Dyer.*

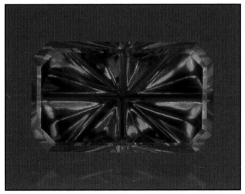

Fig. 2.28 Untreated Bolivian ametrine (67.92 cts) Nebula ™ Cut. *Cut by John Dyer & Co; photo by Lydia Dyer.*

Fig. 2.29 Untreated Tanzanian ruby (1.04 cts) StarBrite™ cut. *Cut by John D. Dyer & Co; photo by Priscilla Dyer.*

Fig. 2.30 Hand carved shell cameo (40 mm). *Necklace and photo: Rainforest Design®.*

Fig. 2.31 Star rose quartz intaglio. *Carved & photographed by Nancy Arthur McGehee.*

Sometimes gems are both faceted and carved. In such cases, they may be identified as either fancy cuts, fantasy cuts or carvings.

Carving

CARVING is a specialized type of cutting which produces intricate designs and forms, not just flat facets or evenly curved surfaces. The first three of the following art forms are considered to be carvings:

ENGRAVING: A shallow design cut into the surface of a stone. The overall shape and contour of the stone is changed very little.

CAMEO: A stone, often banded chalcedony, with a design or picture cut in relief. The background is removed to expose the desired picture.

INTAGLIO: An engraved stone with a figure or design carved into its surface.

GEMSTONE BLENDED WITH A PHOTO TO RESEMBLE AN INTAGLIO PORTRAIT: Two examples are the Spencer Portraits™ in figures 2.32 & 2.33, which are modern interpretations of historical portrait jewelry. They are a new category of gemstone art that blends natural gem materials such as rock crystal and mother of pearl with photography of a loved one, pet, wild animals, abstract patterns or landscapes.

Fig. 2.32 Spencer Portrait™. *Brooch by Melissa Spencer; photo: Dimaond Graphics.*

Fig. 2.33 Spencer Portrait™. *Brooch by Melissa Spencer; photo: Diamond Graphics.*

The best known type of carvings are **SCULPTURES**—stones cut as three-dimensional objects such as a figurines or abstract forms as in figures 2.34–2.36.

Fig. 2.34 Baker Ranch, New Mexico agate. *Fantasia carvings and photo by Glenn Lehrer.*

Fig. 2.35 Agate Fantasia carving in Mexican agate in the ballerina motif, right: Brazilian dendritic agate carving in the angel motif. *Carved & photographed by Glenn Lehrer.*

Fig. 2.36 Mother of pearl, Siberian chatoyant nephrite; gold plated bronze casting of an actual *Tridacna gigas* known as Giant Clamshell; Clear Creek, California jadeite pearl; Edwards Black, Wyoming jade base. *Jade carving and photo by Georg Schmerholz.*

Miniature carvings like those in figures 2.37 & 2.38 can be worn as gems in jewelry.

Fig. 2.37 Aquamarine (27.67 cts) carved by Sherris Cottier Shank. *Photo:Amy Balthrop.*

Fig. 2.38 Golden beryl (4.56 cts) carved by Sherris Cottier Shank. *Photo: Amy Balthrop.*

A gemstone with carved areas and a free form may have some of the same characteristics as a traditional cut—it may be partially faceted or cabbed, and it may have a crown, girdle and pavilion. In the trade, this type of gemstone may be called a **fantasy cut** or **fancy cut** (figs. 2.39 & 2.40).

Gemstone carvers and faceters have similar goals—to bring out the brilliance and color of a gem. However, instead of simply using small flat planes to accomplish this, gem carvers may also use grooves, curved planes, recessed areas and undercutting, which create a wide variety of effects.

Fig. 2.39 Citrine (13.36 ct) cut by John Dyer. *Necklace by Hubert; photo by Diamond Graphics.*

Fig. 2.40 Fancy-cut aquamarine (47.20 cts) carved by Dalan Hargrave. *Aquamarine from Mayer & Watt; photo by Geoffrey Watt.*

Many talented artists have become involved in gemstone carving because it offers the opportunity to work in a sculptural manner with beautiful color and fascinating optics. As a result, there are many new styles of cutting. Some modern carvers may cut a deep three-dimensional pattern into a stone with a crown, girdle and/or pavilion. The depth of cutting creates a play of light that is as important as the carving pattern itself. Some cutters may concentrate primarily on optical effects and others may depart entirely from recognized gemstone shapes, creating a gem that is entirely free-form.

Carvings are usually priced per piece instead of per carat. Their value depends on the skill and fame of the cutter, the type of material used, the time required to execute the design, the fame of the carving's owner(s), and their antique value if any. Custom-crafted, one-of-a-kind designs are naturally more expensive than those that are mass produced or machine-made.

Sometimes designers accept nature's handiwork and use natural crystals or stones with a natural crystal face in their jewelry pieces (figs. 2.41–2.44). It has also become popular to use crystal accumulations called druse. See next section.

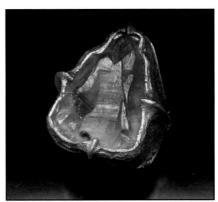

Fig. 2.41 Mint tourmaline crystal. *Ring by Katy Briscoe; photo by Kennon Evett.*

Fig. 2.42 Amethyst natural surface. *Ring and photo by Catherine & Michael Jensen.*

Fig. 2.43 Labradorite natural surface. *Ring and photo by Catherine & Michael Jensen.*

Fig. 2.44 Blue chalcedony natural botryoidal surface. *Pendant by* Zaffiro; *photo by Elizabeth Gualtieri.*

Fig. 2.45 Drusy quartz (54.09 cts) with natural dendrite crystal inclusions. *Pendant by Hubert; photo by Diamond Graphics.*

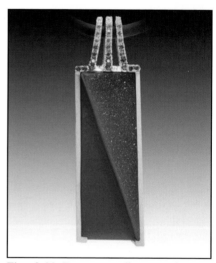

Fig. 2.46 Drusy carnelian. *Pendant by Sugarman-Franz Designs; photo by Michael Sugarman.*

Drusy Gem Materials

Druse is a crust of tiny crystals on the surface of a rock or mineral. If the crust is garnet, for example, then it's called drusy (or druzy) garnet. Even though the base of the druse is normally not garnet, the combined base and crust are also called drusy garnet. The base is a natural part of the drusy material; it's *not* a backing that's glued to the crust. "Drusy" is also used as a noun, so "garnet drusy" equals "drusy garnet."

Most drusy material is untreated. Two exceptions are drusy black onyx, which is dyed black chalcedony and titanium drusy agate. It's coated with titanium in a vacuum chamber as a vapor deposition, producing sparkly shades of tanzanite blues.

One important element in the evaluation of drusy is coverage. Crystal coverage relates to whether areas of the underlying host rock show. Top-grade drusy pieces have a sparkly, uninterrupted, thick pile of fine- to medium-grain bright crystals with highly saturated colors. Lower grades look dull and sometimes show areas of the base rock.

To clean drusy stones, use water and a soft cloth and blot dry with a paper towel or cloth. It's best to avoid soaps and detergents because they can leave a film which may cling to the textured druse. In addition, avoid using brushes on coated drusies because they may damage the coating.

Trapiche Stones

Some stones have natural patterns that are prized in the gem trade. For example, trapiche gems have a star pattern formed by inclusions or zoning and are cut as cabochons or slices (figs. 2.47-2.50). *Trapiche* is the Spanish word for the cogwheel used to grind sugar cane. It has an appearance similar to that of trapiche stones.

Fig. 2.47 Trapiche chalcedony from Mogok, Burma. *Gem: Jeffery Bergman; photo by Jeff Scovil © Primagem.*

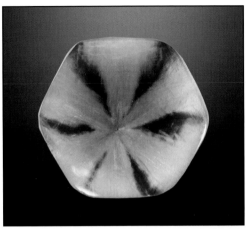

Fig. 2.48 Trapiche sapphire (8.30 ct) from Mogok, Burma. *Gem: Jeffery Bergman; photo by Jeff Scovil © Primagem.*

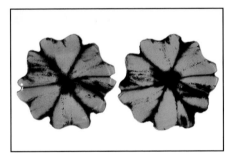

Fig. 2.49 Emerald trapiche slices (4.94 cts) from Mayer & Watt. *Photo by Geoffrey Watt.*

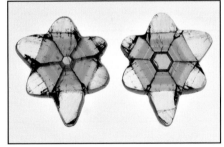

Fig. 2.50 Emerald trapiche stars (14.56 cts) from Mayer & Watt. *Photo by Geoffrey Watt.*

In the past half century, two opposite trends have emerged. On one hand, designers are selecting unpolished crystals and rocks or crystal slices for their jewelry. On the other hand, gem cutting has become much more complicated and technical. Designers and cutters are now more creative than ever. They are transforming druse, trapiche stones and low-priced gem materials such as quartz, chalcedony and blue topaz into distinctive jewelry pieces and spectacular works of art. Thanks to the greater emphasis on high-quality cutting, it's easier to find stones with pizazz than it was thirty years ago. For a better idea of what types of styles are now available, go to your local jeweler and ask to see some of the contemporary cuts and new gem materials. Don't forget your wallet. When you see how pretty these gems are, you'll want to own some.

3

Carat Weight

The term "carat" originated in ancient times when gemstones were weighed against the carob bean. Each bean weighed about one carat. Gem traders were aware, however, that the weights varied slightly. This made it advantageous for them to own both "buying" beans and "selling" beans.

In 1913, carat weight was standardized internationally and adapted to the metric system, with one carat equaling 1/5 of a gram. The term "carat" sounds more impressive and is easier to use than fractions of grams. Consequently, it is the preferred unit of weight for gemstones.

The weight of small stones is frequently expressed in **points**, with one point equaling 0.01 carats. For example, five points is the same as five one-hundredths of a carat. Contrary to popular belief, jewelers do not use "point" to refer to the number of facets on a stone. The following chart gives examples of written and spoken forms of carat weight:

Table 3.1

Written	Spoken
0.005 ct (0.5 pt)	half point
0.05 ct	five points
0.25 ct	twenty-five points or a quarter carat
0.50 ct	fifty points or a half carat
1.82 cts	one point eight two (carats) or one eighty-two

Note that "point" when used in expressing weights over one carat refers to the decimal point, not a unit of measure. Also note that "pt" can be used instead of "ct" to make people think for example, that a stone weighs 1/2 carat instead 1/2 of a point.

Size Versus Carat Weight

Sometimes in the jewelry trade, the term "size" is used as a synonym for "carat weight." This is because size and weight are directly related. However, as gems increase in weight, their size becomes less predictable. This means a 0.90-ct emerald, for example, may look bigger than a 1.05-ct emerald. Therefore, you need to consider stone measurements as well as carat weight when buying colored stones. You don't need to carry a millimeter gauge with you when you go shopping. Just start noting the different illusions of size that various stone shapes and measurements can create.

Fig. 3.1 The emerald (1.24 ct) looks almost twice the size of the ruby (1.11 ct), which has a similar weight and depth. The sapphire in the center weighs 2.73 cts, but it does not look double the size of the emerald. Since emeralds are not as dense as rubies and sapphires, emeralds appear larger. *Photo © by Renée Newman.*

You should also note that one gem species can have different measurements than another gem species of the same weight. For example, because of its higher density, a one-carat ruby is considerably smaller than a one-carat emerald. Rubies and sapphires are heavier (more dense) than diamonds and most colored stones. One major exception is garnet. Depending on the type, garnets may have a similar or greater density than corundum stones.

We can compare gem sizes by comparing their **specific gravity** (a ratio comparing the weight of a gem to an equal volume of water at 4°C). The specific gravity of emerald is about 2.72, whereas that of corundum (ruby and sapphire) is about 4.00. The specific gravity of diamond is about 3.52.

Effect of Carat Weight on Price

Most people assume that when purchasing gemstones, the higher the carat weight, the greater the value. However, they may not realize that a one-carat ruby, for example, is worth far more than several small rubies of similar quality with a total weight of one carat. This is because the supply of large rubies is more limited. So when you compare jewelry prices, besides noting the quality, you should pay attention to individual stone weights and **notice the difference between** the labels **1 ct TW** (one carat total weight) **and 1 ct** (the weight of one stone).

When comparing the cost of transparent gems, you should also start noting the **per-carat cost** instead of concentrating on the total cost of the stone. This makes it easier to compare prices more accurately, which is why dealers buy and sell most gems using per-carat prices. However, many opaque and translucent stones such as jade, malachite and chalcedony are sold by the stone or piece, not by weight. Designer cuts may also be priced per piece, and colored stones under about a half carat are often priced according to millimeter size. The following equations will help you calculate the per-carat cost and total cost of gemstones:

$$\text{Per-carat cost} = \frac{\text{stone cost}}{\text{carat weight}}$$

$$\text{Total cost of a stone} = \text{carat weight} \times \text{per-carat cost}$$

The price/weight categories of colored gems vary from one dealer to another, so there's no point in listing any. Just be aware that carat weight can affect the per-carat value of gemstones and follow these two guidelines:

♦ Compare the per-carat prices of transparent gems instead of their total cost.

♦ When judging prices, compare stones of the same size, shape, quality and color.

Estimating Carat Weight

If you buy jewelry in a reputable jewelry store, you normally don't need to know how to estimate the carat weight of gems because the weight will be marked. However, if you buy jewelry at flea markets or garage sales, it is to your advantage to know how to estimate weight.

Appraisers estimate the weight of faceted gems by measuring their length, width and depth with a millimeter gauge (these are sold at jewelry supply stores). Then they calculate the weight with formulas such as the ones found in Table 3.2. The only accurate means of determining the weight of a stone is to take it out of its setting and weigh it. This, however, is not always possible or advisable.

Table 3.2 Weight Estimation Formulas for Faceted Gems	
Round	Diameter^2 x depth x S.G. x .0020
Oval	Diameter^2 x depth x S.G. x .0021 (Average out length & width to get diameter)
Rectangular Cushion	Diameter^2 x depth x S.G. x .00235 (Average length and width to get diameter)
Square Emerald Cut	Length x width x depth x S.G. x .0023
Rectangular Emerald Cut	Length x width x depth x S.G. x .0027
Square (with corners)	Length x width x depth x S.G. x .0025
Rectangular Baguette	Rectangular Baguette
Pear	Length x width x depth x S.G. x .0020
Marquise	Length x width x depth x S. G. x .0021
Heart	Length x width x depth x S.G. x .00195

Note: S.G. = Specific Gravity. The specific gravity of the major gems is given in Chapter 11, "Gemstone Descriptions." The above formulas are based on stones with medium girdles, no pavilion bulge, and well-proportioned shapes. Thick girdles may require a correction of up to 10%. Bulging pavilions may require a correction as high as 18%. The correction for a poor face-up shape outline can be up to 10%. For further information on weight estimation, consult the *Complete Handbook of Weight Estimation* by Charles Carmona.

4

Judging Color

Depending on whom you talk to, sherry-colored topaz is either yellow, orange, yellowish brown or reddish. That's because people have different opinions as to what the color of sherry looks like. Color terms like "sherry" "champagne" and "cognac" are great for displays and advertisements, but they're not appropriate for lab reports, appraisals and serious gemological texts because such terms don't provide an accurate visual idea of gem color.

Expressions like "grass green" are not much better. This term has been used in gemological literature to describe the color of peridot, alexandrite viewed outdoors, and fine emerald. That's understandable because grass comes in a wide range of greens. Most grasses, however, tend to be grayish or brownish, so it would be difficult to find grass with a top-grade emerald color.

For a more precise and accurate description of gems, it's helpful to divide color into the three components below. There are other ways to break down color but this book uses the system employed by the Gemological Institute of America (GIA).

HUE: Refers to the basic spectral colors of blue, green, yellow, orange, red, purple and violet as well as transition colors such as bluish green and yellowish green. (Sometimes people are uncertain about the difference between purple and violet. Violet falls between blue and purple. Purple is between red and violet so it is redder than violet.) Brown, black, gray and white are not considered to be hues because they're not part of the color spectrum.

TONE (LIGHTNESS/DARKNESS): Refers to the amount of color. In some color systems, this is called "value" or "saturation." The lightest possible tone is colorless. The darkest is black. Tone is described in this book by the following terms:

very light	medium	very dark
light	medium dark	
medium light	dark	

SATURATION: The strength, purity, vividness or intensity of the hue (also called chroma in color science); the degree to which the hue is hidden by brown or gray. When the saturation decreases, cool hues like green, blue and violet generally become grayish, and warm hues like red, orange and yellow usually become brownish. Therefore, a brownish red stone has lower saturation than an orange-red stone with the same tone. In most cases, the higher the color saturation, the more valuable the stone.

The GIA color saturation scale uses "vivid" as the highest of six color saturation levels followed by "strong" and "moderately strong." The other levels in the order of their descending saturation level are:

- very slightly brownish or very slightly grayish
- slightly brownish or slightly grayish
- brownish or grayish

A term such as "strong medium green" is less ambiguous than expressions like "grass green" and "sherry-colored." However, it's not as precise as using a color master stone or color sample as a reference point for describing gem color.

Not everyone has the same visual image of strong medium green. So keep in mind that the color descriptions in this book are general, not precise. Nevertheless, they're better than "grass green," "pigeon-blood red" and "cornflower blue," terms which have often been used to describe the top color of emerald, ruby and sapphire.

COLOR DISTRIBUTION & UNIFORMITY (COLOR COVERAGE) is a fourth factor that should be considered when evaluating gemstone color of both faceted and unfaceted gemstones. Top quality jade cabochons have a uniform color throughout the stone. The more uneven or blotchy the color is, the lower the value. However, jade with multiple colors within the same stone can be very expensive if the colors are intense and distinct.

Faceted gems typically display some extinction, which are dark black or gray areas seen through the crown. The amount of extinction you see depends on the tone, the cut, the type of lighting and the distance of the light from the stone. Light-colored, shallow-cut stones normally show less extinction than those which are dark-toned or deep-cut. As the light source gets broader, more diffused, and/or closer to stones, they display less extinction and more color. In general, the higher the degree of color coverage, the more valuable the gemstone. Color zoning tends to lower stone prices, but in some cases the zoning makes the stone more unique and attractive, thereby increasing its value.

Fig. 4.1 Contrasting saturation. A ruby with good color saturation flanked by two rubies with a much less valuable brownish red color. *Center ruby from Andrew Sarosi; photo © Renée Newman.*

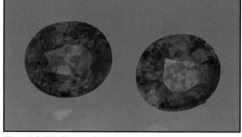

Fig. 4.2 Well-matched Burma rubies (total weight 4.02 ct) with a higher percentage of strong red color coverage than the rubies in figure 4.1. *Rubies from Robert Kane & Fine Gems International; photo © Harold & Erica Van Pelt.*

Fig. 4.3 Lavender jadeite arranged in ascending order of retail value. Because of its grayish color, #1 would cost the least—about $180 as of this book's publication date. Cabochon #7 would cost about $8400 because of its strong, uniform pinkish lavender color and high clarity. The bluish mottled and moderately grayish color of #2 reduces its value to about $400. The paleness of #3 sets its retail value at $720. The deeper color of #4 increases its value to $1700, but its mottling keeps it price below the $2400 price of #5, which has a nice pinkish lavender color. The stronger lavender color of #6 raises its retail price to about $4200. Note: the actual colors of these stones may be slightly different than shown. The printing and developing processes usually alter the true color of gems in photographs. *Burma jadeite courtesy Mason-Kay; photo © Renée Newman.*

Fig. 4.5 Burma ruby (3.33 cts) with excellent color. *Ring & photo: ColorMasters Gem Corp.*

Fig. 4.6 A Madagascar sapphire (7.54 cts) with excellent color. *Ring & photo: ColorMasters.*

Fig. 4.7 Emeralds with excellent color. *Earrings by Hubert Inc; photo by Diamond Graphics.*

Fig. 4.8 North Vietnamese red spinel (2.20 cts) with excellent color. *Ring by Thomas Dailing, spinel cut by Richard Homer, photo by Azad.*

Fig. 4.9 Top grade ammolite. *Pendant & photo: Korite Intl.*

Fig. 4.10 Ammolite with lower brightness and color saturation. *Gem & photo: Korite Intl.*

Fig. 4.11 A mostly green bright ammolite. *The Jeweler's Bench, Inc; photo; Skip Colflesh.*

Evaluating the color of gems with color phenomena is more complex than for other gems. The ammolite stone on the left is of exceptional quality because it has a brilliant and diverse color display (including the rare blue). Also, unlike most ammolite stones, there are hardly any dark areas or lines interrupting its color.

Evaluating Gemstone Color

Even though it's debatable as to which are the most valuable hues and tones, gem dealers agree that highly saturated, vivid colors are far more desirable than dull, muddy ones. In most high-quality stones, the bright areas of color are not grayish or brownish.

Judging the **lightness or darkness** of a faceted gemstone is difficult because it doesn't display a single, uniform tone. It can have light and dark areas which become more apparent as you rock the stone in your hand. To judge the tone of a faceted gem, examine it face-up and answer the following questions:

◆ What is your first overall impression of the tone? How does it compare to that of other stones of the same variety? Use words such as "light" and "medium light" to describe tone, but keep in mind that the tonal boundaries of these terms can vary from one person and grading system to another. In most cases, medium to medium-dark tones are more valued than light and very dark tones.

   The depth of color can play a major role in the price of gems. For example, a strong blue tanzanite selling for $5000 might cost less than $1000 if it were very light blue. There's nothing inherently wrong, however, with light-blue tanzanites. In fact, they can be quite flattering to people who look good in pastel colors. It's just that there is a much greater demand for deep-blue tanzanite.

◆ Do you see near colorless, washed-out areas in the stone? This is a symbol of insufficient color, poor cutting or both.

◆ What percentage of the stone looks black? If more than 90% of a stone is blackish, gem dealers would classify it as undesirable, assuming that the stone is not black onyx or some other normally black stone. Many low-priced sapphires look black. Good sapphires are blue.

Fig 4.4 Sapphires with colors ranging from good (left) to low grade (right) viewed on a white paper with a desk lamp. The sapphire on the right is too black, and the sapphire next to it looks washed out because of an undesirable "window" (a see-through effect caused by poor cutting).

Judging the **hue** of a stone is just as difficult as judging the tone. The different tones within it are distracting. Moreover, it may be a blend of two or three colors. When you look at the stone from different directions while moving it, you can see the different colors. This is caused by certain optical properties of the stone, which are discussed in Chapter 11, "Gemstone Descriptions." This chapter also indicates the most valued hues for many of the important gem varieties. To determine the hue, look for the dominant color in the face-up view. Go with your first overall impression. Keep in mind that the most expensive hues are not necessarily the ones which will look best on you. If you don't plan to resell your stone, there's no need to base your choice of hue on trade preferences. Just choose the color you like best and that fits your budget.

How to Examine Color

When selecting a gemstone, follow these steps:

◆ Clean the stone with a soft cloth if it's dirty. Dirt and fingerprints hide color and brilliance.

◆ Examine the stone face up against a variety of backgrounds. Look straight down at it over a non-reflective, white background and check to see if the center of the stone is pale and washed out. (This is undesirable). Then look at it against a dark background. Do you still see glints of color or does most of the color disappear? Also, check how good the stone looks next to your skin.

◆ Examine the stone under direct light and away from it. Your stone won't always be spotlighted as you wear it. Does it still look colorful out of direct light? It should if it's of good quality.

◆ Look at the stone under various types of light available in the store. For example, check the color under an incandescent light-bulb, fluorescent light, and next to a window. If you're trying to match stones, it's particularly important to view them together under different lights. Stones that match under one light source may be mismatched under another.

◆ Every now and then, look away from the stone(s) and glance at other colors and objects to give your eyes a rest. When you focus too long on one color, your perception of it is distorted.

◆ Rotate the stone and examine it for **color zoning**—the uneven distribution of color. When the color is uneven or concentrated in one spot, this can sometimes decrease the stone's value. It can also present a problem if the stone is recut. The color may become lighter. Obvious color zoning is most serious when visible in the face-up view of a stone.

◆ Compare the stone side by side with other stones of the same variety. Color nuances will be more apparent.

◆ Make sure you're alert when you examine stones. If you're tired, sick, or under the influence of alcohol or drugs, your perception of color will be impaired.

How Lighting Affects Gemstone Color

When buying gems, consider the lighting because it has a strong impact on your impression of the color and brilliance of gemstones. An indirect neutral light like noon daylight is often recommended for grading gemstones. Its color temperature ranges from about 5000-5500K and doesn't favor either end of the color spectrum. Incandescent light bulbs, battery-powered flashlights and some halogen spotlights will shift the color balance of light from neutral towards the yellow or warm end of the spectrum, intensifying the appearance of red and orange colors. Daylight fluorescent lights and overcast skies produce light spectrums that contain more blue wavelengths. This strengthens blue colors and makes reds look more purplish and greens and purples look more bluish.

When you shop for gems, your choice of lighting will probably be limited. However, try to view the gems under different light sources such as slightly bluish fluorescent lights, slightly yellowish halogen lights, LED lights and daylight near a window. Keep in mind that each of these light sources can have different color temperatures. For example, fluorescent lights can lean to the blue or yellow end of the color spectrum or have a neutral 5000-5500K color temperature. The color temperature of light outdoors also varies throughout the day. It goes towards the yellow at sunrise and sunset; towards the blue under clouds or blue skies and towards neutral at noon.

5

Judging Clarity & Transparency

Clarity is the degree to which a stone is free from flaws. Gemologists call flaws *within* a stone **inclusions**. Flaws on a stone's surface are **blemishes**. A general term for inclusions and blemishes is **clarity characteristics.**

Clarity and transparency are important value factors for gems, sometimes even more important than color. Consider, for example, emeralds or sapphires. No matter how grayish, brownish, and/or light-colored they are, they are still gems if they are transparent and **eye-clean** (free of inclusions visible to the unaided eye; the term **clean** by itself can mean that a stone is of high clarity). However, if the stones are nearly opaque and filled with deep cracks and eye-visible inclusions, they're industrial grade stones, even if they have a desirable color.

Some gems, such as emeralds, rubies and red beryl typically have numerous inclusions so there's a greater tolerance for a lower clarity in these gems than for those which commonly have a high clarity, e.g., aquamarine, blue zircon, citrine, green tourmaline, kunzite, morganite and topaz. Some colored gems that fall between these high- and low-clarity groups include blue tourmaline, blue sapphire, garnet, iolite, peridot, spinel and zircon that is green, orange or red.

Even though inclusions often have a negative impact on value, their presence can be positive. Inclusions help identify your stone if it gets lost or stolen. They are especially important as evidence that your stone is natural. Jewelers and dealers are suspicious of flawless rubies and emeralds because that's usually a sign the stone is man-made. Certain inclusions, such as fine silk-like fibers, help prove that a gem is untreated. Inclusions can also increase the value of a stone by helping to prove that it's from a location such as Kashmir. (Certain places have a reputation for producing top-quality gemstones). Sometimes inclusions add value to a gem simply because of their beauty as in figure 5.2. With colored gems, it doesn't matter whether a stone is flawless or not; what matters is the types of flaws that are present and whether they have a negative impact on appearance and/or durability.

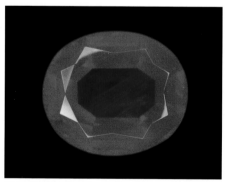

Fig. 5.1 The barely visible silk in this Burma ruby indicates that its rare color is natural and not the result of heat treatment. *Ruby (5.90 carats) and photo from Jack Abraham.*

Fig. 5.2 The inclusions in this dendritic agate increase its value. *Pendant by Patrick Murphy and Emily Chesick; photo by Corey Morse.*

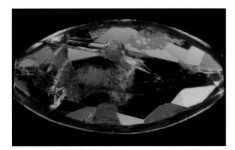 

Figs 5.3 & 5.4 Two views of a ruby with undesirable inclusions, including a long crack and concentrations of red dye. *Photos © Renée Newman.*

Transparency

Transparency is the degree to which light passes through a material so that objects are visible through it. Transparency and clarity are interlinked because flaws can block the passage of light. Gemologists use the terms below to describe gem transparency.

♦ **Transparent**—objects seen through the stone look clear and distinct.

♦ **Semitransparent** —objects look slightly hazy or blurry through the stone, but it is easy to read print through the material.

♦ **Translucent**—cloudy and milky, like frosted glass. Depending on the color and thickness of the stone, objects may or may not be visible through the material.

♦ **Semiopaque**—only a small fraction of light passes through the stone, mainly around the edges. Print is not visible through the opaque areas.

♦ **Opaque**—no light can pass through the gemstone. Hematite is an example of an opaque gem. Most stones identified as opaque gems are technically semiopaque because light can pass through their edges or through thin slices of the material.

Occasionally, **near transparent** is used as a category between transparent and semitransparent. The most transparent specimens of jade and opal can fit in this category as well as many high-quality rubies, sapphires and emeralds.

Another word that refers to transparency is **texture.** AGL (American Gemological Laboratories) in New York applies this term to fine particles which interrupt the passage of light in a material. The finely divided particles are not detrimental to the durability of a stone, but they can have an adverse effect on its appearance. Yet texture is not always a negative factor. The texture within Kashmir sapphire, for example, gives it a prized velvety appearance. AGL, on its lab documents, describes the texture (transparency) of colored stones as transparent, faint, moderate, strong or prominent.

Dealers often use other terms to designate gem transparency, some of which are:

♦ crystal (highly transparent)   ♦ cloudy
♦ highly transparent   ♦ looks like soap
♦ milky   ♦ sleepy (low transparency)

Jade dealers often use **translucency** instead of the term "transparency." Dealers of opal, another nearly opaque to near transparent gem, generally prefer to use "transparency."

For the sake of consistency, this book uses "transparency" for all gems when referring to how easily light can pass through them. It's easier to understand gemstone evaluation when the same terminology is used for every gemstone. Whether a gem is traditionally considered as transparent or translucent, transparency can play a major role in its value. Don't overlook this when comparing the prices of gemstones.

Gemstone Inclusions

Opinions differ as to how various clarity features should be classified. Some feel the term "inclusion" should be reserved for foreign matter within a stone. This book uses a broader definition, which is found in the GIA gemstone courses: "**Inclusions** are characteristics which are entirely inside a stone or that extend into it from the surface." The GIA defines **blemishes** as "characteristics confined to or primarily affecting the surface."

As you examine stones under magnification, you may wonder what inclusions you are looking at. Listed below are gemstone inclusions found in colored stones:

◆ **Crystals** are solid mineral inclusions of various shapes and sizes. Minute crystals that look like small specks under 10X magnification are sometimes called **pinpoints** or **grains**. Crystals lower the clarity, but they can also turn a stone into a collector's item if they are unusual and attractive. The larger and more visible the crystals are, the more they impact the clarity.

◆ **Negative crystals or voids** are hollow or fluid-filled spaces inside a stone that have the shape of a crystal. They often resemble solid crystals, so for purposes of clarity grading, they're called "included crystals."

◆ **Silk** in gemstones consists of very fine fibers of minerals such as rutile (titanium dioxide). The fibers can also be made of mineral grains arranged in straight rows. These fibers or rows intersect and resemble silk, hence the name. Well-formed silk can be proof that a stone was not heat-treated to improve its color. Very high temperatures tend to dissolve it and make it look fuzzy or dot-like. Since untreated stones tend to be more valued than treated ones, the presence of clear, well-formed silk can be a welcome sign.

Fig. 5.5 Colorful crystal inclusions in quartz. *Photo by Lucas Fassari.*

Fig. 5.6 Pyrite inclusions in quartz. *Photo by Lucas Fassari.*

Fig. **5.7** Needle inclusions in Deer Creek, AZ fire agate. *Photo by Dennis Walters.*

Fig. **5.8** Crystal, fingerprint & pinpoint inclusions in tanzanite. *Photo © Renée Newman.*

♦ **Needles** are long, thin inclusions that are either solid crystals or tubes filled with gas or liquid, which are called **growth tubes**.

♦ **Clouds** are hazy or milky areas in a stone. Most clouds are made up of crystals too tiny to see individually under ten-power magnification; they can also be composed of fluid drops rather than solids. When clouds are large and dense, they diminish transparency.

♦ **Cracks** of various sizes are not uncommon. They may also be called **fractures, fissures** or **breaks**. When they're straight and flat, they're called **cleavages**. Because of their appearance, cracks are sometimes called **feathers**. Normally, you need not worry about cracks if they are small. However, if they are deep or long, they can threaten the durability of the stone. The location of the cracks is also important. Surface cracks on the table of a stone have a negative impact on value. A crack in the center of the stone is much easier to see with the naked eye than one close to the edge.

♦ **Halos** are circular fractures surrounding a crystal. These structures generally result from tension created by the growth of the crystal inside the halo or by heat treatment.

♦ **Fingerprints** are partially healed cracks. Many colored gems grow from a mineral solution, and if they split during formation, the solution can fill the cracks and let them grow back together. During this healing process, stray drops of liquid are sealed in and form patterns that look like human fingerprints.

♦ Fluid inclusions are hollow spaces filled with fluid. They occur in random shapes and sometimes are so dense that the stone may look milky.

Fluid inclusions are classified into three types: **single-phase**, a void containing only fluid; **two-phase**, a liquid and a gas or two nonmixable liquids; and **three-phase**, a liquid, a gas and a solid. These inclusions provide clues about the origin of a stone. Colombian emeralds, for example, are noted for their jagged-edged, three-phase inclusions which contain a salty liquid, gas bubble(s) and salt (halite) crystal(s). Indian emeralds often have parallel two-phase inclusions.

Fig. **5.9** Three-phase inclusions in Columbian emerald. *Photo: George Bosshart.*

Fig. 5.10 Two-phase inclusions in beryl. *Photo by Lucas Fassari.*

Fig. 5.11 Three-phase inclusion in quartz. *Photo by Lucas Fassari.*

◆ **Cavities** are holes or indentations extending into a stone from the surface. Cavities can result when solid crystals are pulled out of a stone or when negative crystals are exposed during the cutting process.

◆ **Chips** are notches or broken off pieces of stone often along the girdle edge or at the culet.

Gemstone Blemishes

◆ **Scratches** are straight or crooked lines scraped on a stone. Since they can be polished away, they don't have much of an effect on the clarity.

◆ **Pits** are tiny holes on the surface of a stone that often look like white dots.

◆ **Abrasions** are rough, scraped areas usually along the facet edges of a stone. They are seen more often on colored stones than on a diamond, due to the diamond's exceptional hardness.

Examining Gemstones for Clarity

To examine a stone for clarity you need a ten-power magnifier, a lint free cloth and a light source with either a translucent shade or a bulb that's frosted—not bare. An ordinary fluorescent desk lamp will do. Tweezers or a stoneholder is also helpful.

Jewelers often use a hand magnifier called a loupe. For those interested in owning a loupe, do an Internet search of "Jewelers' Supplies" in your area. Verify that they have a fully corrected, ten-power, triplet loupe. The loupe salesman or a jeweler can show you some ways of holding and using it and help you select the model that is the most comfortable and clear. Plan on paying at least $25 for a good loupe. Cheaper types, which are not fully corrected, tend to distort objects.

When using a ten-power loupe, hold it about 1/2 to 1 inch (13-25 mm.) away from the stone to bring it into focus. If you're examining a large stone, hold the loupe close to one eye (about 1 or 2 inches or 25-50 mm. from the eye) keeping both eyes open. The closer the loupe is to your eye, the greater your field of vision will be.

Often it's easier for lay people to examine stones through a microscope. Many jewelers own microscopes and encourage their customers to use it when purchasing gemstones.

Fig. 5.12 A 10-power triplet loupe

When you have the necessary equipment, you can proceed as follows:

◆ **Clean the stone**. Otherwise, you may think dirt and spots are inclusions. Usually rubbing it with a lint-free cloth is sufficient. If you're examining jewelry at home, it may have to be cleaned with water. (See Chapter 11 for cleaning instructions.) Professional cleaning might also be necessary. Avoid touching the stone with your fingers because fingers can leave smudges.

◆ **Examine the entire stone without magnification**. (However, if you require eyeglasses for reading, you'll need to wear them when examining gems.) One of the main criteria for assessing the clarity of colored gems is the visibility of the inclusions with the unaided eye. Looking at the stone first with a loupe or microscope can mislead you into believing inclusions are eye visible when they aren't, because your mind has a tendency to see what it expects to see. So check to see if there are any noticeable flaws *before* using magnification. If you are looking at a good topaz, aquamarine or tanzanite, you shouldn't see any. A good ruby or emerald, on the other hand, is likely to have eye-visible inclusions. However, the fewer flaws it has, the higher its value.

◆ **Check the overall transparency of the stone.** If your goal is to buy a high-quality transparent gemstone, avoid stones that are cloudy to opaque.

◆ **Look at the stone from several angles**—top, bottom, sides. Even though top and centrally-located inclusions are the most undesirable in terms of beauty, those seen from the sides or bottom of a stone can affect its price or durability.

◆ **Look at the stone with light shining through it from the side** (transmitted light). This will help you see inclusions and fractures inside the stone. It will also help you judge transparency.

◆ **Look at the stone with light shining on it from various angles**—above it, through the sides, and reflected off the surfaces. Overhead illumination will help you determine what the blemishes and inclusions look like under normal lighting conditions. Light transmitted through the sides will highlight inclusions and will usually make them more visible. Light reflected off the surface will help you identify surface cracks and blemishes.

◆ **When you judge clarity, compare stones of the same type**. Emeralds, for example, should be compared to emeralds, not to other gems, which usually have a higher clarity. Green tourmaline, a typically transparent, clean stone, should be compared to other green tourmalines, not to green garnets or red tourmalines, which tend to be more included.

◆ **Keep in mind that light-colored stones should have a better clarity than darker ones.** In lighter stones, inclusions are easier to see. Dark colors often mask flaws.

◆ **Remember that prongs and settings can hide flaws.** If you're interested in a stone with a high clarity, it may be best for you to buy a loose stone and have it set.

◆ **Keep in mind that your overall impression of a stone's clarity can be affected by the stones it is compared to.** A stone will look better when viewed next to one of low clarity than next to one of high clarity. To have a more balanced outlook, try to look at a variety of qualities.

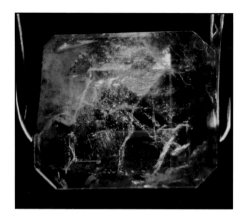

Figs. 5.13 & 5.14 Two views of an emerald with liquid inclusions and fractures—one in darkfield illumination under 10-power magnification and another in overhead lighting with less magnification. *Photos © Renée Newman.*

How Lighting Can Affect Your Perception of Clarity

You should judge the clarity of colored stones using overhead lighting both with and without magnification. A loupe (hand magnifier) or a microscope can help you see potentially damaging fractures that might escape the unaided eye.

When people use microscopes to judge clarity, they usually examine the stones with a type of lighting called **darkfield illumination**. This is a diffused lighting that comes up diagonally through the bottom of the stone. (A frosted or shaded bulb provides **diffused** light, a clear bulb does not.) In this lighting, tiny inclusions and even dust particles will stand out in high relief. As a result, the clarity of the stone appears worse than it would under normal conditions (figures 5.13 to 5.16 provide examples of this).

Overhead lighting is above the stone (not literally over a person's head). It is reflected off the facets whereas darkfield lighting is transmitted through the stone. When looking at jewelry with the unaided eye, you normally view it in overhead lighting. However, if you ask salespeople to show you a stone under a microscope, it is unlikely that they will use its overhead lamp. Instead they may only have you view the stone under darkfield illumination.

When judging colored-stone clarity under magnification, you should use overhead lighting for the following reasons:

◆ **Dealers use overhead lighting when pricing gems**. They typically examine stones under a fluorescent lamp with and without a loupe (usually 10-power).

◆ **Overhead illumination is a natural way of lighting which does not exaggerate inclusions.** It therefore helps you make a fair assessment of a stone's appearance.

◆ **Overhead lighting does not hide brilliance**. The prime reason for looking at gems through loupes and microscopes is to see their beauty and brilliance magnified. Darkfield illumination masks brilliance. Consequently, it prevents you from making an accurate global assessment of a gem under magnification.

After using overhead lighting, you should also view stones under darkfield illumination. It highlights inclusion details which are useful for detecting synthetics, treatments, and place of origin. With emeralds, for example, darkfield illumination can help one determine the depth of cracks, the type of filling present in fractures, and the extent to which an emerald may have been treated to hide cracks. In summary, darkfield lighting is a useful diagnostic aid, but it can be misleading when used for judging the clarity of colored gemstones.

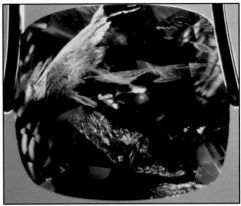

Fig. 5.15 An iolite in overhead light. From the standpoint of appearance, the clarity is not bad. However, large fractures in the stone threaten its durability. *Photo © Renée Newman.*

Fig. 5.16 Darkfield illumination turns the hardly noticeable fractures into distracting inclusions. Ten-power magnification through a microscope was used for this stone in both photos. *Photo © Renée Newman.*

Do We Need Grades to Evaluate Clarity and Transparency?

The diamond industry has a standardized system for grading clarity based on a system developed by the GIA. Ten-power magnification is used. The advantage of having this system is that buyers can communicate what they want anywhere in the world. In addition, written appraisals and quality reports are more meaningful.

One of the drawbacks of the diamond grading system is that it has sometimes caused buyers to become so focused on color and clarity that they overlook brilliance and cut. Another drawback is that it has led people to judge stones by grades rather than with their eyes. No grade or lab report can give a full picture of what a stone looks like. In addition, grades are often misrepresented. Without examining a stone under magnification, one cannot tell if a grade has been inflated.

Even though clarity grading systems have been developed for colored stones, there is no one standardized system. Even when a single system is used, there can be a wide variation in how grades are assigned by appraisers, mainly because the way in which transparency is incorporated into the system may differ. Therefore, it's best for you to ask appraisers what their grades mean. Grades are helpful for documentation purposes, but you don't need them to judge clarity and transparency.

6

Judging Cut Quality

Cut plays a major role in determining the value of colored gems because it affects their color and clarity as well as their brilliance. For example, a stone that is cut too shallow can look pale and lifeless, and it can display flaws that would normally not be visible to the naked eye.

The term **cut** is sometimes confusing because it has a variety of meanings. Jewelers use it to refer to:

♦ The **shape** of a gemstone (e.g. round or oval)

♦ The **cutting style** (e.g. cabochon or faceted, brilliant or step cut, single or full cut)

♦ The **proportions** of a stone (e.g. pavilion depth, girdle thickness)

♦ The **finish** of a stone (e.g. polishing marks or smooth, flawless surface; misshapen or symmetrical facets)

The proportions and finish are also called the **make** of the stone. Proportions and how they affect the appearance of colored gems will be the focus of this chapter. Shape and cutting style were discussed in Chapter 2. Finish won't be discussed because it usually has little effect on the price of colored stones. If there is a problem with the finish, it can usually be corrected by repolishing the stone. Blemishes such as scratches and abrasions are sometimes considered as part of the finish grade of the stone. This book classifies them as clarity elements.

Judging the Face-up View

Colored stones should display maximum color. However, if they're cut with improper angles, their color potential can be diminished with what is called a **window**—a washed out area in the middle of the stone that allows you to see right through it. Windows (or windowing) can occur in any transparent, faceted stone no matter how light or dark it is and no matter how deep or shallow its pavilion. In general, the larger the window, the poorer the cut. Windowed stones are the attempt of the cutter to maximize weight at the expense of brilliance.

Fig. 6.1 Print seen through a large window

To look for windows, hold the stone about an inch or two (2 to 5 cm) above a contrasting background such as your hand or a piece of white paper. Then try to look straight through the top of the stone without tilting it, and check if you can see the background or a light window-like area in the center of it. If the stone is light colored, you might try holding it above a printed page to see if the print shows through. If the center area of the stone is pale or lifeless compared to a darker faceted area surrounding the pale center, this is also a window effect. The best cut stones show no window even when tilted back and forth.

Figs. 6.2 & 6.3 Before and after view of a sapphire (4.25 ct / 3.10 ct) whose pavilion and crown were recut to remove windowing, improve symmetry and to ensure even brilliance across the stone. *Cut by J. L. White Fine Gemstones; photos by Jeff White.*

Figs. 6.4 & 6.5 Before and after view of a sapphire (4.89 ct / 4.00 ct) whose pavilion was recut to remove windowing and improve color and brilliance. *Cut by J. L. White Fine Gemstones; photos by Jeff White.*

When evaluating a stone for windowing, you will probably notice dark areas in it. The GIA refers to these as **extinction areas** or simply **extinction**. All transparent faceted gems have some dark areas. However, a good cut can reduce extinction and increase color. One should expect dark stones to have a higher percentage of dark areas than those which are lighter colored. You should also expect there to be more extinction than what you see in pictures of gems. During shooting, photographers normally use two or more front lights to make stones show as much color as possible. When you examine a stone, you will usually be using a single light source, so less color and more black will show. The broader and more diffused the light, the more colorful the stone will look. Therefore, compare stones under the same type and amount of lighting.

The quality, complexity and originality of the faceting should also be considered when judging cut. Some of the best faceting is done on low- and medium-priced gem material such as topaz aquamarine, garnet, quartz, tanzanite and tourmaline. The faceting and proportioning of more expensive stones like emeralds and rubies is often less precise because the higher cost of the rough leads many cutters to be more interested in retaining weight than in maximizing beauty. Finding an emerald or ruby without windowing can be difficult. Nevertheless, emeralds, rubies and other expensive stones can be well-cut and display good color and brilliance. For more photos and information on faceting styles, see Chapter 2.

When you hear the term **brilliance** used, keep in mind that it has different definitions. In the GIA Colored Stone Grading Course, it is defined as the percentage of light return in a gem after the percentage of windowing and extinction are subtracted. AGL (American Gemological Laboratories) uses "brilliance" only in connection with the amount of windowing present. A stone with no window whatsoever would receive a brilliance grade of 100%. Such a high brilliance percentage would not be possible under the GIA system because there is always some extinction present in transparent faceted gems. In this book, the term "brilliant" is used in the colloquial sense of having both a high intensity and large area of light return. A dull-looking, low-transparency stone with no window would not be described as "brilliant" under this non-technical definition.

Fig. 6.6 A very brilliant citrine (28.28 cts) from Rio Grande del Sul, Brazil. No windowing is present; extinction areas are minimal and intense color is displayed over the entire gem. *Citrine cut by Mark Gronlund; photo by Robert & Orasa Weldon.*

When judging the face-up view of a gem, another factor to consider is the outline of the shape. If it's a standard shape that should be symmetrical, check to see if it is. If you plan to resell the stone later, make sure it's a shape others might like. A very long, skinny marquise or emerald cut, for example, may be hard to sell. With stones such as ruby, emerald and alexandrite, conserving weight from the rough is often more of a priority than good symmetry.

Judging the Profile

When you buy a gemstone, be sure to look at its profile. The side view can indicate:

◆ If the stone is suitable for mounting in jewelry.

◆ If the stone will look big or small for its weight.

◆ If the cutter's main goal was to bring out the stone's brilliance.

When evaluating the profile, hold the stone with the shortest side facing you (widthwise) and **check the overall depth** (referred to in the trade as the **total depth percentage**). If you look at it lengthwise, the stone could look too shallow when in fact it may have an adequate depth. You should expect well-cut colored stones to be deeper than diamonds, which have a high refractive index (a measure of the degree to which light is bent as it travels through a gem).

Noted mineralogist John Sinkankas makes this point in his book, *Emerald and Other Beryls* (page 334): "In the case of higher refractive index gemstones, inner reflections can result from shallower bottom angles, thus allowing these gems to be cut less deeply. This becomes apparent when two brilliant gems of the same size and style of cutting are compared, one being diamond and the other a beryl. It will be seen that the diamond is cut to less depth while the beryl had to be cut to greater depth in order to insure upward reflection of light."

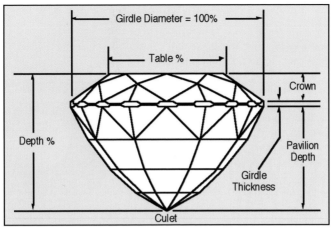

Fig. 6.7 Profile diagram of a mixed-cut colored stone. *Copyright 1978 by American Gemological Laboratories, Inc.*

The **total depth percentage** of the stone in the profile diagram of figure 6.7 can be calculated as follows: **depth**

width (girdle diameter)

In this case, the total depth percentage is 65%, which is a good depth/width ratio for a colored stone. There are differences of opinion as to which is the best depth percentage for a colored stone cut in a traditional style such as an emerald cut or round brilliant cut. Some say 60 to 65%. Others say 65 to 80%. Combining these two ranges, we can conclude that a stone's depth should range between 60 to 80% of its width with a more precise percentage depending on the refractive index and shape of the gemstone and the cutting style.

If a stone is too deep, it may not be suitable for mounting in jewelry and it will look small for its weight in the face-up view. The main reason for cutting extremely deep stones is to save as much weight from the original rough as possible. Stones may also be cut deep to darken their color, especially if they are pale or color-zoned. Unnecessary weight adds to the cost of the stone since prices are calculated by multiplying the weight times the per-carat cost. Consequently, when you compare the prices of stones, you should consider their overall depth.

If a stone is extremely shallow ("flat") when you look at it widthwise, it might be fragile and therefore unsuitable as a stone for an everyday ring (it could, however, be good for a pendant, brooch or earrings). Very shallow stones look big for their weight in the face-up view, but unfortunately they often have big windows and lack brilliance, which brings down their value. The main reason for cutting extremely shallow stones is to maintain the shape of the original rough so as not to lose too much weight. Stones may also be cut shallow to lighten their color.

Some cutters are able to take flat gem rough and cut it into attractive, brilliant stones using non-traditional cutting styles (fig. 6.8). The Torus Ring™ is an example of this. Its face-up view is larger than a normal stone of the same weight without any sacrifice to brilliance. In this case, the total depth percentage of the gemstone is irrelevant. What matters is the overall appearance.

When judging the profile of a gemstone, you should also pay attention to the **crown height and the pavilion depth.** Notice the relationship of the crown height to the pavilion depth in the profile diagram of figure 6.7 (about 3.5 to 1). Then compare the profile views of gemstones that you own. Without even measuring the stones, you can make visual judgments about their pavilion and crown heights.

If the **crown** is too low, the stone will lack sparkle. When light falls on a thin crown, there tends to be a large sheet-like reflection off the table facet instead of twinkles of light from the other crown facets. Some cutters intentionally cut stones with no crowns in order to draw your eye into the interior of the stone. This is commonly seen in fantasy-style cuts. These stones should be judged on their general appearance, not according to traditional standards.

If the **pavilion** is too flat or too deep, the stone may lack life, have a window, or look blackish. In order for the stone to effectively reflect light, the pavilion and crown must be angled properly. But they can't have the proper angles if they don't have the proper depth.

When evaluating the profile, look at the curvature of the pavilion outline. A

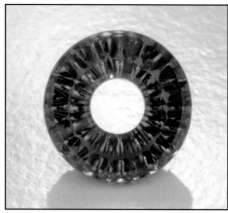

Fig. 6.8 Natural color multicolor Paraiba tourmaline. This is an example of how a skilled, imaginative cutter can bring out brilliance and color, yet minimize weight loss in flat rough. *TorusRing™ cut by Glenn Lehrer; photo by Robert & Orasa Weldon.*

lumpy, bulging pavilion decreases brilliance and helps create dark or window-like areas in the stone. This is because the pavilion is not slanted at an angle that will maximize light reflection. A bulging pavilion is not uncommon in expensive stones in which the cutter is trying to maximize weight. Its another example of how you can end up paying for excess weight that reduces the beauty of the stone. Unlike diamonds, colored stones should have a slight pavilion curvature. This helps decrease windowing as the stone is tilted.

Notice, too, the **symmetry** of the profile. Symmetry problems such as an **off-center culet** prevent light from reflecting evenly. (In cushions, ovals and marquises, the culet should be centered widthwise and lengthwise. In hearts and pear-shapes, the culet should be placed at the widest portion of the stone.) It's common for rubies, emeralds, sapphires and alexandrites to look less symmetrical than stones such as diamonds. However, when stones are so lopsided that their brilliance is seriously diminished, the lack of symmetry is unacceptable.

Also check the **girdle width**. Stones with very thin girdles are difficult to set and easy to chip. Stones with thick girdles have reduced brilliance, look smaller than they weigh, and are also difficult to set. The judgment of girdle thickness is best done with the eye, with and without magnification. If the girdle looks like a wide band encircling the stone, it's probably too thick. If the girdle is sharp and you can hardly see it, then it's probably too thin. **Wavy and uneven girdles** can also create setting problems. In addition, they indicate that the cutter did not pay much attention to detail.

For a more in-depth discussion of the cut evaluation of faceted colored gemstones consult the article by Al Gilbertson on the "Value factors, Design and Cut Quality of Colored Gemstones (Non-Diamond)" in the March/April 2016 issue of the *Gem Guide* "Gem Market News."

7

Star & Cat's-Eye Stones

Cabochons (gems with a domed, polished surface) can resemble a cat's eye when they have many needle-like inclusions or hollow tubes, all parallel to each other, and are cut properly. When the cabochon is placed under a concentrated light source such as a light bulb, a band of reflected light is visible across the top of the cabochon. This effect is called **chatoyancy**, and stones that display it are said to be **chatoyant**. *(Chat* means "cat" in French.)

The term "cat's-eye" when used by itself also refers to the chatoyant variety of chrysoberyl, a gem species. Other minerals such as beryl, quartz, tourmaline and zircon can also display a cat's-eye, but these stones must include the mineral name—for example, "cat's-eye quartz" or "quartz cat's-eye." Besides the cat's-eye effect, these stones may show what is called the "**milk and honey effect**" (fig. 7.2)—when the stone is held with the eye at a right angle to a beam of light, the half of the stone nearest the light shows the body color of the stone, while the other half looks milky. When the stone is rotated between two lights, the chatoyant band appears to open and close. The open position is shown in figure 7.4.

Top-quality cat's-eye stones have the following characteristics:

♦ They have a sharp, straight, narrow band (eye) positioned in the center of the cabochon. The band is distinct and not too thin.
♦ The band of reflected light is white or gray, not the same color hue as the stone's background.
♦ The eye extends all the way across the stone.
♦ The stone has no distracting flaws.
♦ The stone is neither opaque or transparent.

Unfortunately, there aren't many stones that meet all these criteria. When buying gemstones it's often necessary to compromise on some quality factors. Don't expect cat's-eye stones to be free of eye-visible flaws or to have perfect symmetry. Don't worry if a little of the stone's color shows through in the eye. The most important consideration when buying a chatoyant gem is that it has a distinct eye.

The needle inclusions in cat's-eye stones line up in one direction like thread on a spool, but in some gems they align themselves in groups oriented in different directions. When these stones are cut as cabochons, the bands of

Fig. 7.1 Diagonally oriented chrysoberyl cat's-eye. *Ring from Lang Antiques, San Francisco; photo by Cole Bybee.*

reflected light may cross each other in the center, creating a star. This effect is called **asterism**. The half of a band that starts from the center of the stone and goes to the edge is called a **ray**. Star gems generally have from four to twelve rays. Star rubies and star sapphires are the best known star gems. Other gems that can display a star include beryl, garnet, quartz and spinel.

Figs. 7.2–7.4 Left to right: Cat's-eye traditional view, milk and honey effect, opening and closing effect. *Cat's-eye from Andrew Sarosi; photos © Renée Newman*

In 1947, synthetic star ruby and sapphire stones were introduced to the market by the Linde Division of the Union Carbide Corporation in the United States. They were an instant success, and ever since that time there has been a tendency to expect natural stones to resemble them. It's true that there are some very fine deep blue and red specimens in museums and private collections, but these are the exception rather than the rule. Most natural star sapphires are normally more pale than natural faceted sapphires, and their stars are not as well defined as those of laboratory-grown (synthetic) stones. Natural star rubies often have a maroon rather than red color and their stars tend to be indistinct and imperfect.

Even though lab-grown star sapphires and rubies usually have sharper stars and a more intense color than a natural stone, they are not highly valued. They can be found in jewelry supply stores for about $10–$50 per stone. (However, some of the newer synthetic stones with lighter colors and more natural looking stars sell for a lot more.) In contrast, a natural stone with a similar color and size but a less perfect star than a $30 synthetic stone could sell for several thousand dollars per carat.

Your main concern when judging the star of a star stone should be: is it easy to see the star when you look at the stone under a single, direct light source such as a penlight or light-bulb? (The star will hardly be noticeable in diffuse light from fluorescent lights or overcast skies.) Secondary questions to ask are:

♦ Is the star centered?
♦ Is the star sharp and well defined?
♦ Are the rays straight?
♦ Are all the rays present?
♦ Do the rays extend completely across the stone?
♦ Is there a good contrast between the star and the background?

Fig. 7.5 Sri Lankan purple star sapphire (6.32 cts). It's unusual to find a natural star sapphire of any color with such a well-centered star, distinct full rays and strong color saturation. *Gem from Pala International; photo by Mia Dixon.*

Fig. 7.6 Mexican star strawberry quartz (49.53 cts) cut by John Sinkankas. *Courtesy Bill Larson of Pala International; photo by Wimon Manorotkul.*

Fig. 7.7 A low-priced Indian star ruby, which is nearly opaque. Photo © Renée Newman.

Fig. 7.8 A much more expensive star ruby with a better clarity and transparency. *Lang Antiques, San Francisco; photo by Cole Bybee.*

Fig. 7.9 Synthetic star ruby. Note how distinct the rays are. *Ring: Lang Antiques, San Francisco; photo by Cole Bybee.*

Ideally you should be able to answer yes to all of the preceding questions. In actuality, however, the stars on natural stones tend to be slightly wavy, a little blurry and/or incomplete. Often the better the color is, the more imperfect the star looks. Appraisers normally indicate the degree to which the stars conform to the above standards. Under the category of star centering, for example, they may indicate poor, fair, good, very good or excellent.

The degree of transparency also plays a major role in determining the value of star gems. As a general rule, the more transparent a star stone is, the greater its value. A translucent Indian star ruby, for example, can sell for a lot more than if it were nearly opaque.

The evaluation of color in star stones is similar to that of faceted stones, but the overall grading is more lenient. Generally, the more saturated and pure the body color, the more valuable the stone will be. Medium and medium-dark tones tend to be the most prized, although light tones are considered acceptable. Natural star sapphires other than the black variety tend to be light blue or gray.

It's normal for star stones to have inclusions. However, the more obvious these inclusions are to the naked eye, the lower the value of the stone. It's usually best to avoid stones with many surface cracks because they may not be very durable, and they may be dyed.

Star gems have often been worn as good-luck charms. In his book, *The Curious Lore of Precious Stones,* George Kunz states that the three cross-bars of the star were thought to represent faith, hope and destiny. Supposedly, star sapphires were so powerful at warding off bad omens that they would exercise their good influence over their first owners even after passing into other hands. Even today, star stones are worn for good luck.

Though rare, natural star gems are available. However, don't expect them to have perfect stars, clarity and symmetry. Stones that meet these criteria are generally synthesized in a factory, not created by nature.

8

Treatments & Processes

A treatment is any action such as heating, oiling, irradiation, waxing, bleaching, dying or impregnation which alters the color, clarity, transparency and/or durability of a stone. Faceting and polishing are not considered treatments even though they usually make gem rough look better.

The term **process** is sometimes used to refer to a series of actions that can change the appearance and durability of gem materials. For example, the Zachary process involves treating turquoise with chemicals and then heating it to improve color and durability. Jadeite is often acid bleached to remove discolorations and impurities and then filled with a polymer and sometimes a dye to improve the transparency and color. However this process makes the jade less durable. It's often referred to as a bleaching/ impregnation treatment, and the resulting product is called "B" jade.

Fig. 8.1 Left: iron-oxide stained natural water worn pebble containing jade. Center: "B" jade that has been cleaned and bleached with acid to remove iron-oxide stains, Right: epoxy-impregnated "B" jade, part of bangle. *Henry A. Hänni © SSEF.*

Gem Treatments

HEAT TREATMENT: For centuries, gems have been heated to improve their color. However, in more modern times, heat treatment has been conducted with more sophisticated techniques and at much higher temperatures—1600°C (2900°F) and above. Besides lightening, darkening or changing the color of a stone, heat can improve its clarity. Unless a receipt or lab document states otherwise, you should assume that the following gemstones have probably been heat-treated: aquamarine, carnelian, ruby, sapphire, tanzanite, pink topaz, green tourmaline and blue zircon.

Heat treating is widely accepted because some say that it's a continuation of a natural process and it usually causes a permanent improvement of the entire stone. From the standpoint of value, it usually doesn't matter whether commercial-quality stones have been heat-treated or not as long as the color is permanent. The overall quality of the treated stone determines the price. However, a premium may be charged for high-quality *unheated* stones that come with a lab report stating there is no evidence of any type of treatment.

IRRADIATION: Various types of radiation are used to intensify or change the color of certain gems. Gamma rays from a cobalt or cesium source are the preferred irradiation agent because they don't induce radioactivity in the treated stones. Pink tourmaline is one example of a stone that is commonly treated with gamma radiation to intensify its color. The strength of the color can be a measure of the dose of radiation the stone received naturally and/or through treatment. The color is relatively stable, but strong heat from lights, for example, may cause it to fade. Fortunately, irradiation treatment will restore the color. Irradiated pink and red tourmalines are free of radioactivity because the gamma treatment does not change the nuclei of their atoms. Instead, some of the outer electrons are moved to different positions, creating what are called *color centers* which change the way the stone absorbs light.

Topaz is another stone that is routinely irradiated. But in order to obtain the desirable intense blue color, the irradiation is done by one of three different processes. In most cases, colorless topaz is irradiated in a high-energy electron-beam linear accelerator and/or nuclear reactor, which usually turns it brown. The topaz is then heat-treated to remove the brown and produce a stable blue color. This irradiation uses much higher energy levels than that for red tourmaline and can result in a change to the nucleus of the atoms of impurities in the topaz, creating radioactivity, which may take a few days to many years to decay. In many countries, treated gems are now regulated and must meet certain standards. The United States has the strictest requirements. When suppliers of blue topaz guarantee that their stones come from a licensed facility that's in compliance with standards set by the Nuclear Regulatory Commission, you need not worry about radioactivity in them.

Other gem varieties that can be enhanced with irradiation include:

Maxixe- (ma SHE she) **type beryl**—dark blue beryl from pale pink or colorless beryl; fades.

Yellow beryl—from colorless beryl; some fades in light or heat.

Green and smoky quartz—from amethyst and colorless quartz (rock crystal); stable.

Yellow or orange sapphire—from colorless and light yellow sapphire; fades in minutes to days   Most yellow sapphire is heat treated, not irradiated.

Diamonds that are green, blue, yellow or brown—from light yellow or brown diamond; stable.

"Black" or **Dark-Color Pearls**—from off-color bleached pearls; stable, after a slight fading just after treatment.

The information on radiation treatment in this section comes primarily from the book *Gemstone Enhancement* by Dr. Kurt Nassau and from personal communication with Dr. Horst Krupp and Dr. Nassau, both physicists, mineralogists and gemologists.

FRACTURE FILLING WITH OIL, WAX, RESIN OR POLYMERS: When surface-reaching fractures in gems are filled with an appropriate substance, they are less noticeable and the overall color and transparency of the stone may improve. Emeralds typically have small surface-reaching cracks so they're commonly filled with oil, wax, resin, polymer or an epoxy-type substance. Unfortunately, the filling can evaporate and may leave a white or brown residue. This is not a major problem if the stone has been oiled because the discoloration can be cleaned out by repeated immersion of the stone in a solvent such as lacquer thinner. Afterwards it can be re-oiled to look as good as when bought. Some hardened epoxies, however, may be difficult to extract. Therefore fillers which are easy to remove and as stable as possible tend to be the preferred types for emerald.

Ruby is another stone that may be oiled or filled with epoxy when surface-reaching cracks are present. Ruby oiling with colorless substances is not as well accepted by the trade as emerald oiling and it's not as common. Sometimes ruby and emerald oils contain a dye. The stability is poor and the color may change over time.

FRACTURE HEALING WITH FLUX: During heat treatment, a flux borax solution used on rubies and sapphires can melt and form a glass that seeps into fractures and cavities. This improves the stone's appearance. This process is often referred to as infilling or fracture-healing. It's less accepted than heat treatment but more accepted than ruby oiling because it's relatively permanent and irreversible. It may also improve a stone's durability since the fractures are healed shut.

The extent of the filling treatment should be a consideration when buying expensive rubies and sapphires. Gem labs now indicate on their documents the extent of the filling, often by describing it as minor, moderate, significant or none. The less filler present the more desirable the gem.

FILLING WITH LEAD GLASS:
Initially this was primarily a ruby fracture filling treatment with molten lead glass, but it has progressed into an impregnation process similar to that of B jade. Poor quality, heavily fractured **corundum** (the mineral name for ruby and sapphire) is treated with acid to remove impurities and then impregnated with a colored lead glass instead of a polymer. Acid substances like lemon juice and household cleaners can cause white spider-web-like lines to form on a stone where the filling is. In extreme cases, tiny pieces of corundum are fused together with lead glass to create a stone; contact with a jeweler's torch during repair may cause such stones to crumble into pieces.

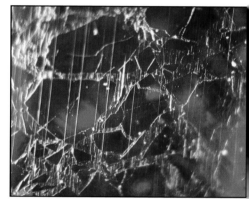

Fig. 8.2 Mosaic-like structure of a lead glass-filled "ruby" magnified and viewed in transmitted light. *Photo: The Gem Testing Laboratory of The Gem and Jewelry Institute of Thailand.*

Some labs call lead glass-filled "rubies" COMPOSITE RUBY, GLASS-RUBY COMPOSITE or HYBRID RUBY because they contain so much glass and do not have the durability of normal gemstones. If the stones have been assembled from tiny pieces of glass and corundum, a lab may identify them simply as a manufactured product. At gem shows, lead glass-filled "rubies" may sell for as little as $5-$50/carat. Many consumers at home and abroad have paid large sums of money for these stones thinking they have bought highly valuable rubies when in fact they have purchased a stone composed primarily of glass that requires special care.

Most lead glass-filled "rubies" are relatively easy for gemologists to identify because they usually display a blue to purple flash effect in fractures or internal cavities when examined with oblique light under magnification. Spherical gas bubbles are typically present.

DYEING (STAINING): Rubies, emeralds, jade, quartz and other stones that may have small surface cracks are occasionally dyed with colored oils and epoxies, especially if they're of very low quality. The dye can sometimes leak out. Some gemstones like lapis lazuli, turquoise, chalcedony and agate don't need surface cracks to accept dye. They are naturally porous and are often dyed with permanent dyes. Black onyx is just dyed chalcedony.

Dyed onyx is well-accepted in the trade, but dyed rubies, emeralds and jade are not. Some dyes can fade over time when exposed to sunlight, Many dyes can be removed if the stone comes in contact with a solvent such as acetone or alcohol. Dye treatments provide a practical means of making low-grade stones look better. Unfortunately, these stones are often sold with the intent of fooling buyers. Then, instead of being a legitimate treatment, dyeing becomes a deceptive practice.

BLEACHING: Chemicals may be used to lighten or remove color. Pearls, coral, jadeite and ivory are commonly bleached.

IMPREGNATION: Some porous gems are impregnated with a colorless melted wax, resin, or plastic-like substance to fill pores, hide cracks and to make the surface look shiny. Impregnation can also improve durability and color. Sometimes dyes are added to the impregnation material. Examples of stones undergoing this treatment are amazonite, coral, jade, lapis, malachite and turquoise. Impregnation with plastic-like substances is sometimes referred to as STABILIZATION. As mentioned previously, often low grade jadeite is impregnated with a polymer and very low grade corundum (ruby or sapphire) is impregnated with a lead glass after having been bathed in acid to remove impurities and discolorations. The acid makes the stones porous.

COATING: Coloring and/or hardening agents are applied to the surface of a stone to change the color or make the stone more scratch resistant. These may be metal oxides or diamond-like thin films created by a chemical vapor deposition (CVD) process.

Some stones that have been coated include topaz, quartz, tanzanite, apatite and diamond. The coating can wear away and may show abrasions or scratches.

Paint, ink, shoe polish, nail polish, varnish and lacquer have also been used to coat gemstones. These types of coatings are normally not disclosed and are therefore considered deceptive practices.

DIFFUSION OF FOREIGN COLORING ELEMENTS: Initially this treatment was done to make the surface area of near colorless sapphires look blue and sometimes red, orange or yellow or to create a star formation. Around 1988, it was also being used on colored sapphires to improve their color. In 1992, reports of red and pink diffusion-treated corundum began to increase. Surface-diffused sapphires and rubies had been heated in the presence of titanium or chromium—coloring elements too large to penetrate far below the surface of the stone. The color is permanent, but remains only at the surface. Consequently, the color can be polished or scraped off, leaving the grey or white interior exposed.

Possibly starting in the late 1990s, some sapphires were heated with beryllium, a small element which allowed the coloration to penetrate the entire stone. Names that have been used for this deeper reaching coloring treatment include **lattice diffusion**, **bulk diffusion**, and **beryllium treatment**. Beryllium treatment has been done mainly to produce pink-orange and yellow sapphires, but it has also been done to make dark sapphires lighter and rubies a more intense red.

The andesine and labradorite varieties of feldspar have been diffused with copper to alter their color. Stones diffused with beryllium or copper cost significantly less than their natural counterparts. The treatment is considered permanent.

RECONSTITUTION / RECONSTRUCTION: Small particles of a natural material are bonded with a resin or another compound into a larger whole. Bonded powdered turquoise is an example of this process. The resulting stone is also called a composite.

9

Synthetic Stones

To the average person, a synthetic is a fake. In the jewelry trade, though, the word **synthetic** is used differently. It describes a gemstone made in a lab which has the same basic chemical composition and similar chemical, optical and physical properties to its natural counterpart. **A natural gemstone** comes from the ground and is a product of nature, not of man. **Imitations**, on the other hand, do not have the same chemical composition as the stones they resemble, and they may be natural in origin or made by man. Red glass, for example, can be a man-made imitation of ruby. Garnets used to mimic rubies would be natural imitations.

Since consumers tend to interpret the word "synthetic" differently than jewelers, people who sell synthetic stones usually prefer to describe them with terms such as **created**, **lab-grown** or **man-made**. Gemologists and natural stone dealers usually identify lab-grown stones as synthetics.

Cultured is sometimes used as a synonym for "lab-grown." The two terms, however, are not equivalent. Culturing pearls is a more natural process than producing gems in labs. A cultured pearl has a nacre coating that is secreted by a natural organism in a natural environment. Man just inserts the irritant into a mollusk. On the other hand, created gems are grown in a lab, not in the ground, and the ingredients are supplied by man, not by nature through a natural process.

Synthetic gems are not just a recent phenomenon. Lab-grown ruby, the first synthetic, has been sold commercially since the early 1900's. Today, lab-grown stones are common, especially in birthstone jewelry and class rings. Synthetics are also found in designer jewelry, set with diamonds in gold or platinum. Some of the stones that may be synthetically produced and sold to consumers in jewelry are:

Synthetic alexandrite	Synthetic citrine	Synthetic opal
Synthetic amethyst	Synthetic diamond	Synthetic ruby
Synthetic aquamarine	Synthetic emerald	Synthetic sapphire
Synthetic beryl (red, yellow)	Synthetic garnet	Synthetic spinel
Synthetic chrysoberyl	Synthetic lapis lazuli	Synthetic turquoise

Some stores call **imitation** stones "synthetic." For example, imitation tanzanite may be incorrectly sold as "synthetic tanzanite" because "synthetic" sounds better than "imitation." Green CZ (cubic zirconia) is often wrongly called synthetic emerald. Green CZ is a lab-grown stone, but it's not synthetic emerald, and it is much cheaper than lab-grown emerald.

Synthetic Versus Natural

Both natural and synthetic stones of the same gem variety have essentially the same chemical composition, hardness, luster and refractive qualities. However, there are some important commercial differences, namely:

Fig. 9.1 Parallel growth zoning in synthetic alexandrite (20x). *Photo by Lucas Fassari.*

Fig. 9.2 Curved growth zoning in synthetic sapphire. *Photo by Lucas Fassari.*

Price: Most lab-grown stones cost much less than their natural counterparts. The price is determined by their availability, the process used to grow them and market competition. When lab-grown ruby first appeared on the market, it cost about as much as natural ruby. Today you can buy the same type of lab-grown ruby for a few dollars a carat. When well-cut, it can be quite attractive. Other synthetic rubies which are grown by a different process may retail for more than $300/ct. This is still much less than if they were natural and had the same color and clarity.

Appearance: One of the biggest advantages of lab-grown stones is that they generally look more attractive and of higher quality than natural stones of the same price. For example, a $200 one-carat synthetic emerald will usually have a more saturated green color and higher clarity than a one-carat natural emerald because the synthetic emerald is grown under controlled conditions. Mining emeralds is a much more time consuming and expensive process than growing emeralds in a factory.

Availability: Lab-grown stones can be produced in whatever quantities are needed. As a result, they are readily available and cost less. High quality natural stones such as emeralds are rare and therefore more valuable. Natural amethyst, on the other hand, is quite common and affordable. Finding a good-quality natural stone in the size or shape you'd prefer is often difficult. You may have to compromise on size, quality, or color.

Emotional Value: Natural gemstones traditionally have an aura of mystery due to their long, intriguing history and the remote places in which they are mined. Consumers interested in the romantic aspects of gems will generally attach a greater emotional value to a natural stone than one created relatively quickly in a laboratory. For discriminating buyers there is no substitute for the "real thing."

Potential for Price Appreciation: Despite market fluctuations, the overall value of natural gems has usually increased over the years. As a result, some have been accepted as a medium of exchange and as collateral for loans. Created gems have not enjoyed this prestige. Instead, their price has generally gone down as production and competition have increased. Rather than being viewed as a portable treasure, synthetic stones are considered an affordable alternative to the natural stone.

The next time you admire an attractive gem that's beyond your budget, ask if it's available as a lab-grown gemstone. If it is, this may be a good option for you. Your friends probably won't know the difference; they'll just compliment you on your good taste and wonder how you could afford such a fine stone.

10

Deceptive Practices

There is no fraud or deceit in the world which yields greater gain and profit than that of counterfeiting gems. (Pliny the Elder, Roman scholar, from his 37th Book of the History of the World, 1st century AD)

Unfortunately, the counterfeiting of gems is as widespread today as ever. There are just more ways of doing it now. In Pliny's day, there were no lab-grown gemstones. Irradiation and diffusion treatments were unknown. There is nothing wrong with synthesizing or treating gems, but fraud occurs when the synthesis, treatment(s) or beautifying process(es) are not disclosed to the customer.

Listed below are practices that are often done with the intent to deceive.

NONDISCLOSURE OF TREATMENT TYPES: It's not sufficient for a seller to simply say that a gemstone has been treated. The type of treatment processes used must also be disclosed because they can have a major impact on the value and durability. For example, in his book *Ruby & Sapphire, A Collector's Guide* (p 312), ruby specialist Richard Hughes writes that "a 5-ct natural ruby of good quality can be worth tens or even hundreds of thousands of dollars per carat. The same quality stone if found to have been heated via low-temperature heating might be worth 10–20% less. If it was found to have been heated with flux, the discount could drop by more than 50%. And if it was found to be glass-filled, it could be worth just a few dollars per carat."

In addition to the vast price differences among the various types of treated rubies, there's also a major difference in their durability. Rubies that have only been heated are resistant to chipping and easy to maintain; they can be cleaned in ultrasonic cleaners and steamers and can remain in a ring during resizing if they don't have fractures and haven't been oiled. Conversely, rubies that have been soaked in acid and then filled with a lead glass lack the durability of natural rubies; they can easily be damaged by ultrasonic cleaners, acids, steamers and jewelers' torches, and they can chip and crack during jewelry repairs or when worn in rings.

Ethical sellers disclose the type(s) of treatments their stones have undergone and warn their customers when special care is required.

PAINTING: You don't have to cover a pale stone with a colored coating to make it look colorful. A little paint in the right spot(s) can do the job. Due to the multiple reflections in a faceted transparent gem, a dab or two of paint on the bottom and/or edge of the stone can make it appear evenly colored when viewed face up. The paint can be hidden by the mounting. Emeralds have at times been colored in this manner. Translucent opal cabochons may be painted black on the bottom to enhance and intensify their play of color. Peacock feathers, multi-colored butterfly wings and mother of pearl have on occasion been placed behind opal to improve color play too. Sometimes purple ink is applied to the backs of yellowish diamonds or under the prongs of the setting to make the diamonds appear almost colorless and more valuable. Since purple is the complimentary color of yellow, it has the effect of absorbing part of the yellow color. As a result, **beware of closed-back settings**. The bottom of the stone may be painted.

FOIL BACKING: For probably 4000 years foil backings have been used to add color and brilliance to gems. As gem-cutting techniques progressed and brought out more brilliance in stones, these backings became less popular. Today foil backings are occasionally found on genuine stones, but they are more likely to be seen on glass imitations. Again, **beware of closed-back settings**. Something such as foil may be concealed underneath the stones, particularly if they are unusually bright. Foil-backed stones are commonly found in antique pieces.

QUENCH CRACKLING: Stones that are quench crackled have been heated and then plunged into cold water. This procedure is done to produce cracks in synthetic stones so they'll look more natural. Sometimes oil or other liquids are forced into the cracks to imitate the fingerprint inclusions found in natural gems. Colorless quartz may be quench crackled so it can afterwards be fracture-filled with colored oil or dyes and used to imitate emerald, ruby or even jade.

COMPOSITE STONES (ASSEMBLED STONES): Stones formed from two or more parts are called **composite** or **assembled stones**. If they're composed of two parts, they're **doublets**. Those consisting of three parts are **triplets**. Assembled opals are one of the most typical composite stones. Opal doublets and triplets are normally disclosed and sold in a legitimate manner so selling them is **not** considered a deceptive practice. Sapphire and ruby doublets, however, are generally used to trick buyers.

The term **composite ruby** can have a double meaning. It can either be an assembled stone or a ruby that's been soaked in acid and then impregnated with a colored glass. Listed below are various types of assembled stones that are sold on the market:

♦ **Natural stone + natural stone of the same gem species**: Natural stones may be glued together for a couple of reasons. One large stone (especially if it's over one carat) can be sold for a higher per carat price than two smaller ones. Also, composite stones may have a more valuable color than their individual parts. For example, pale yellow sapphire pieces may be cemented with a blue glue to form a blue sapphire, or opal with a play of color may be glued to common opal. Fusing is another method of joining stones.

♦ **Natural stone + synthetic stone of the same gem material**: This is one of the most common types of composite stones. When examined under magnification, it may appear completely natural due to the presence of natural inclusions. The pavilion may be, for example, a deep blue synthetic sapphire, and the crown might consist of pale natural sapphire. The resulting stone is deep blue. Ruby doublets with a synthetic ruby pavilion and a thin natural sapphire crown are quite common.

♦ **Natural stone + glass or a different stone**: One of the best known composite stones is the garnet and glass doublet. It was invented in the mid 1800's to imitate gems of every color. It's a more suitable imitation than glass because the garnet crown is more durable and adds luster to the stone. If you own or have an interest in antique jewelry, you should be especially aware of these doublets. Many of the expensive-looking stones in antique pieces (especially those of the latter half of the 19th century) are nothing but garnet and glass doublets. Today garnet and glass doublets are rare. Glass has also been glued to other stones such as quartz and tanzanite. Slices of opal may be glued to glass, ironstone or black onyx.

♦ **Natural stone + colored glue or gelatin layer + same or another stone**: In Europe and the British Commonwealth countries, this type of assembled stone is called a doublet or **soudé stone** (French for "soldered stone)." In the United States, they're often called triplets. An emerald triplet in the U.S., for example, consists of two pieces of pale emerald that are joined together with a third layer of green gelatin or cement.

A thin slice of opal cemented with black glue to another material such as potch opal, chalcedony or glass can resemble black opal. This stone is called an **opal doublet**. If it also has a protective top of colorless quartz or glass, it is called an **opal triplet**.

The key to identifying a composite stone is to find where its parts have been joined together. This can often be seen by immersing the stone in water (immersion tends to make color differences and the glue layer more obvious). Do not immerse assem-

Fig. 10.1 Colorless beryl triplet. Green cement is third layer. © *R. Newman.*

bled opals in water or other liquids; just look at them from the side. Magnification is another helpful identifying technique. It can reveal separation lines, flattened air bubbles between the parts or swirly areas where the stone has been brushed with glue.

Misnomers

Sometimes gems are sold under misleading names. For example, a garnet may be called an "American ruby" or "Cape ruby" to make it seem more valuable. If a salesperson adds a qualifying word or prefix to a gem name, ask him or her to explain what it means. Some misnomers are:

Oriental amethyst	purple sapphire	California moonstone	chalcedony
Ceylon diamond	zircon	Black onyx	dyed chalcedony
Brazilian diamond	colorless topaz		
Herkimer diamond	rock crystal quartz	Ceylon opal	moonstone
Mogok diamond	topaz	Slocum opal	an imitation opal
Brazilian emerald	green tourmaline	Balas ruby	spinel
Evening emerald	peridot	Bohemian ruby	garnet
Indian emerald	dyed crackled	Brazilian ruby	topaz
	quartz	California ruby	garnet
Medina emerald	green glass	Cape ruby	garnet
Oriental emerald	green sapphire	Colorado ruby	garnet
Spanish emerald	green glass	Siberian ruby	tourmaline
Soudé emerald	green composite	Spinel ruby	spinel
	stone		
		Brazilian sapphire	tourmaline or
Amazon jade	amazonite feldspar		topaz
Australian jade	chrysoprase	Lux sapphire	iolite
Colorado jade	amazonite feldspar	Meru sapphire	tanzanite
Indian jade	aventurine quartz	Oriental sapphire	chrysoberyl
Korea jade	serpentine	Spinel sapphire	spinel
Pikes Peak jade	amazonite feldspar	Water sapphire	iolite
Oregon jade	dark green jasper		
Swiss jade	dyed chalcedony	Oriental topaz	yellow sapphire
		Madeira topaz	citrine quartz
German lapis	dyed blue jasper	Mystic topaz	a coated topaz
Swiss lapis	dyed blue jasper	Smoky topaz	smoky quartz
		Spanish topaz	citrine quartz

11

Gemstone Descriptions

The *Gemstone Buying Guide* is designed to help you evaluate the quality of colored gems. That's why six of the preceding chapters were about gemstone value factors. This chapter will give you some brief information about the history, sources and characteristics of the most important gemstones on the market. Before we begin, here is some basic terminology you should know:

Gemstones may be identified as a group, species or variety. A **group** is composed of a number of closely related species. "Garnet" is an example of a group name. A **species** name refers to a mineral with a characteristic crystal structure and chemical composition. Grossular is one of the species of the garnet group. A **variety** name is normally based on color, transparency or optical effects such as color changes and star patterns; but sometimes the variety name stems from the gem's early history when chemical analyses and crystal structure determinations did not exist. Tsavorite is a green variety of grossular. Amethyst and rock crystal are varieties of quartz. They both have the same essential chemistry and crystal structure but differ in color.

Trade names or **commercial names** are often given to gemstones by dealers to help promote their stones. "Tsavorite" is a trade name that is shorter and more marketable than "transparent green grossular," which is technically a more correct term. **Misnomers** are names that do not correctly identify a gem. Two examples of misnomers are "Herkimer diamond" for colorless quartz and "Kashmir sapphire" when used for sapphire that is not from Kashmir.

Sometimes people classify diamonds, rubies, sapphires and emeralds as **precious** gems, and other stones such as garnet or opal as **semiprecious**. This is misleading. Some garnets and opals sell for several thousand dollars per carat. On the other hand, there are semiopaque rubies and sapphires that sell for less than $10 a carat. In certain contexts, "precious stone" may refer to any stone that is used as a gem. "Precious topaz" can mean real topaz as opposed to citrine quartz or it can refer to high-quality topaz. Since the terms "precious" and "semi-precious" are so confusing, many experts have recommended that they not be used to classify gems.

Each gem species has characteristics which distinguish it from other species. For easy reference, we'll list some of these characteristics below with their definitions.

REFRACTIVE INDEX (RI): the degree to which light is bent as it passes through the stone. This is measured with an instrument called a refractometer. Most colored gems have RI's that range between 1.43 and 1.98. Diamonds have an RI of approximately 2.42, which means they bend light about 2.42 times more than air does. This also means that light travels 2.42 times more slowly through diamonds than it does through air. As a general rule, the higher the RI is, the greater the potential brilliance of the stone. Other factors such as clarity, cut and color also affect brilliance. There can be some variation in the RI of a species depending on a stone's origin and color. This is because of the presence of impurities, which can vary according to the source of the stone. Thus the RI of a species may fall slightly above or below the RI ranges listed in this book.

SPECIFIC GRAVITY (SG): the ratio of a gem's density to the density of water. The higher the SG, the greater the density is. The SG of most colored gemstones falls between 2.00 and 4.75.

HARDNESS: the resistance of a gem to scratching and abrasion. This can be classified using the Mohs scale of hardness. The Mohs scale rates the relative hardness of materials with numbers from 1 to 10. The 10 rating of a diamond is the highest and the 1 of talc is the lowest. The intervals between numbers on the scale are not equal, especially between 9 and 10. Ruby and sapphire rate a 9, but a diamond may be over 100 times harder. Some gems like diamond even have a directional hardness where one direction or surface is harder than another.

TOUGHNESS: the resistance of a gem to breaking, chipping or cracking. This is a different property than hardness. Jade is a relatively soft gem material (6–7), yet it is the toughest.

CLEAVAGE: the tendency for a mineral to split along crystal planes, where the atomic bonding is weak. A gemstone may have one or more directions of cleavage, which are classified as perfect (almost perfectly smooth), distinct or indistinct. Cleavage has a negative impact on toughness.

CRYSTAL SYSTEM: one of the seven classifications of the internal structure of a crystal. It is based on the symmetry of the crystal structure. The simplest and most symmetrical system is called isometric or cubic. The other six systems in the order of their decreasing symmetry are tetragonal, hexagonal, trigonal, orthorhombic, monoclinic and triclinic. For descriptions and diagrams of the seven crystal systems, consult: www.webmineral.com/crystall.shtml.

Materials which don't have a crystalline structure (e.g. glass) are called **amorphous.** Some gems such as jade and agate are composed of minute crystals intricately grown together. These gems are technically classified as aggregates (AGG) and are usually translucent to near opaque.

OPTIC CHARACTER: the effect a gem material has on light. If it can split light into two rays, each travelling at different speeds, then it is **doubly refractive (DR).** If it does not split light, the stone is **singly refractive (SR).** In a doubly refractive gem, there is either one or two directions in which light is not split as it passes through it. In other words, a DR stone will behave as if it is singly refractive in at least one direction. The directions of single refraction are called **optic axes**. If the stone has one direction of single refraction, it is **uniaxial**, if it has two, it is **biaxial**.

Doubly refractive gems will have two RI's if they are uniaxial and three RI's if they are biaxial. The numerical difference between the highest and lowest RI is called the **birefringence** or **birefraction**. When you look through stones with a high birefringence, such as peridot, zircon or calcite, inclusions and facet edges will appear to be doubled. This book does not provide birefringence data, but it gives the optic sign (+ or -). If a uniaxial gem is positive, the lower RI is constant and the higher variable. A negative sign would indicate the reverse. If a biaxial gem is positive, the intermediate RI is closer to the low RI. If negative, it's closer to the high RI.

PLEOCHROISM: the ability of certain gem materials to exhibit different colors when viewed from different directions under transmitted light. A ruby, for example, may appear purplish red in one direction and orangy-red in another. Since it can show two colors, it is **dichroic**. Stones like tanzanite, which can display three colors, are **trichroic**. The strength of pleochroism can range from very strong to very weak. In pastel and colorless stones, pleochroism may not be visible.

Much of the identification data on the following pages was taken from *Gems* by Robert Webster and the GIA *Gem Reference Guide*. Consult these two sources for more information as well as Alan Hodgkinson's 2015 book *Gem Testing Techniques*.

elow is a chart which lists the groups and species of gems in this chapter in the order in which
ey are presented. It indicates if their name is a group, species or variety classification.

Group	Species or Type	Varieties
Quartz	Single or twin crystal, or coarse crystal aggregate	Amethyst, ametrine, citrine, quartz cat's-eye, quartzite, rock crystal, rose quartz, smoky quartz, tiger's-eye
Quartz	Cryptocrystalline quartz (chalcedony)	Agate, bloodstone, carnelian, chalcedony, chrysocolla chalcedony, chrysoprase, jasper, onyx, plasma, sard
None	Chrysoberyl	Alexandrite, cat's-eye, yellow, green or brown (chrysoberyl)
Beryl	Beryl, pezzottaite	Emerald, green beryl, aquamarine, heliodor, Maxixe beryl, morganite, goshenite, bixbite, cat's-eye beryl
Garnet	Andradite, spessartine, pyrope almandine, grossular	Demantoid, topazolite, melanite, rhodolite, hessonite, mali garnet, tsavorite, malaia garnet
None	Cordierite	Iolite
Pyroxene	Jadeite (jade)	Green, lavender, "red," gray or white (jadeite)
Amphibole	Actinolite/tremolite (jade)	Nephrite, green, black, brown or white (nephrite)
Sodalite	Lazurite	Lapis lazuli, sodalite
None	Malachite	
Feldspar	Microcline, orthoclase, albite, anorthite	Adularia, amazonite, golden labradorite, moonstone, peristerite, spectrolite, sunstone
None	Opal	Common, white, black, boulder or fire (opal)
Olivine	Forsterite	Peridot, chrysolite
Pyroxene	Spodumene	Kunzite, hiddenite, green spodumene
None	Corundum	Ruby, sapphire, padparadscha, star ruby, star sapphire
Spinel	Spinel	Red, pink, orange, blue or star (spinel)
Epidote	Zoisite	Tanzanite, thulite, green zoisite, pink zoisite
None	Topaz	Pink, red, yellow, orange, blue, green or colorless (topaz)
Tourmaline	Elbaite, dravite, schorl, liddicoatite	Green, pink, red, yellow, orange, blue, watermelon, colorless, cat's-eye, bi-color (tourmaline), indicolite
Turquoise	Turquoise	
None	Zircon	Blue, green, red, yellow, orange or brown (zircon)

Amethyst & Other Quartz Stones SiO_2—silica (macrocrystalline quartz)

Amethyst—February birthstone and 6th wedding anniversary stone; Citrine—alternate birthstone for November and 13th wedding anniversary stone

Throughout history, supernatural powers have been ascribed to amethyst, rock crystal and other quartz stones. Amethyst, supposedly, could prevent drunkenness and protect people from contagious diseases. Rock crystal spheres have been used to foretell the future. Quartz does in fact have properties that make it seem magical. When quartz crystals are compressed in a certain direction, they become electrically charged. And if you run an electrical current through a piece of quartz, the crystal will vibrate at a single, constant frequency which is determined by the thickness of the crystal and the strength of the current. This is why synthetic quartz crystals are used to regulate watch movements and the electronic frequencies of radios.

Quartz may be the oldest gemstone known to man. In Europe, rock crystal objects have been unearthed with the remains of prehistoric man (20,000 BC). Archaeologists have also found amethyst beads, seals and good luck charms in Egypt which date back to before 3100 BC.

Quartz can occur as single or twinned crystals like amethyst and citrine or as coarse aggregates of tiny crystals as in quartzite. Quartz may also consist of crystals so tiny they can only be seen if you view a thin slice of the stone under high magnification. This quartz is called chalcedony, or more technically **cryptocrystalline quartz.** Chalcedony is discussed in a separate section. Quartz in visible crystals has the following properties.

RI: 1.544–1.553 (constant)	**SG**: 2.64–2.66	**Hardness**: 7	**Crystal System**: Trigonal
Pleochroism: weak to moderate	**Toughness**: Good	**Optic Char**: DR uniaxial positive or AGG	

Cleavage: Imperfect rhombohedral

Reaction to Heat: Strong heat may change the color of amethyst, rose quartz and smoky quartz. Sudden temperature changes can cause fracturing or cleaving.

Stability to Light: Some rose quartz and amethyst may fade.

Care Tips: Ultrasonics are usually safe, but use caution. Avoid acids, alkalies, steamers & strong heat.

Treatments: Citrine—usually heated; amethyst & ametrine—sometimes heated; smoky & green quartz —commonly irradiated; rose quartz—sometimes irradiated; tiger's eye—commonly heated or dyed

Quartz Varieties & Trade Names

AMETHYST: (Purple or violet quartz): The most expensive color is an intense, deep, evenly-colored purple with flashes of red under incandescent light, and the least costly is pale lavender. High-clarity amethyst is readily available at low prices. Retail prices range from about $5–$100/ct. Four major sources are Brazil, Uruguay, Bolivia and Zambia. A lot of synthetic amethyst, citrine and other colors of synthetic quartz are made in Japan and especially in Russia. Some amethyst is heated to lighten its color or to transform it into citrine and sometimes green quartz. Green and yellow quartz can be irradiated to produce amethyst. Amethyst may fade from heat treatment or long exposure to sunlight.

Fig. Am.1 Untreated Bolivian ametrine (46.22 cts). *Cut by John Dyer & Co; photo by Prisceilla Dyer.*

Fig. Am.2 Rock crystal dancer with opal and diamond accents. *Brooch designed and carved by Peggy Croft; photo by Harold & Erica Van Pelt.*

Fig. Am.3 Rutilated quartz and dendritic agate. *Pendant by Patrick Murphy & Emily Chesick; photo by Hanna Cook-Wallace*

Fig. Am.4 Green quartz (prasiolite). *Earrings by Hubert Inc; photo by Diamond Graphics.*

Fig. Am.5 Arizona Four Peaks amethyst. *Commercial Mineral Company / Michael Romanella.*

Fig. Am.6 Citrine. *Bracelet & photo courtesy Erica Courtney.*

Am.7 Amethyst & strawberry quartz. *Different Seasons Jewelry. Photo by Jessica Dow.*

AMETRINE: (Purple- and yellow-zoned quartz, i.e., amethyst + citrine): This popular gem is mined commercially in Bolivia and has only been available since the late 1980's. Its two colors allow cutters to create stones and sculptures with striking zonal patterns. Ametrine retails from about $5–$80/ct, depending on size and quality.

AVENTURINE: This is a translucent to semi-opaque rock called quartzite (technically, a polycrystalline aggregate of quartz grains) with a glittery effect caused by mica inclusions. Aventurine is typically green, but it may also be gray, yellow or brown.

CITRINE (Yellow or orange quartz): Most citrine is heat-treated amethyst or smoky quartz. Natural-color citrine is rare and is usually pale yellow. Its name is derived from the French word for lemon—*citron*. A lot of citrine is sold as topaz. It retails for around $4–$75/ct. Designer cuts may cost more.

GREEN QUARTZ (PRASIOLITE) Even though some green quartz occurs naturally in Brazil, Poland and Canada, almost all of the material sold today is irradiated and heated amethyst.

QUARTZ CAT'S-EYE: Sri-Lanka, India and Brazil are sources of quartz cat's-eye. It may be white, green, yellow or brown. Cat's-eye quartz typically ranges from about $10–$70 per cabochon.

ROCK CRYSTAL (Colorless quartz): This is the most widely distributed variety of quartz. Nowadays, the term *crystal* by itself usually means fine-quality glass. *Crystal* comes from the Greek word for ice—*krystallos*. Besides being cut as beads and faceted stones, rock crystal is used for lenses and all sorts of decorative objects. Sometimes, it may be quench-crackled (heated and cooled immediately) and then dyed green or red to imitate emerald and ruby.

ROSE QUARTZ (Pink quartz): Typically translucent, rose quartz is sometimes irradiated to intensify its color. It costs about $5–$30 per stone, and occasionally shows a star effect.

RUTILATED QUARTZ: This is colorless transparent quartz that has needle-like inclusions of the mineral rutile. Most of it comes from Brazil, but some is from Madagascar. Commercial quality cabs from Brazil retail for about $5-15/ct. Tumbled beads sell for much less. When cut into unusual shapes, rutilated quartz can sell for up to $1000 per piece. Exceptional pieces cut by expert cutters have sold for as much as $5000. Specimens with the rutile in the form of a star are the most highly valued.

SMOKY QUARTZ (Brown to black quartz): Even though smoky quartz is found worldwide, some of it on the market is irradiated rock crystal and this tends to be very dark. When it is from the Cairngorm Mountains of Scotland, it is called **Cairngorm**. This quartz is often sold incorrectly under the misnomer "smoky topaz." Prices can range from around $5–$50 per stone. Black smoky quartz is also called **MORION**.

STRAWBERRY QUARTZ: Found in Mexico and Kazakstan, this is a rare pink to red quartz colored by red needlelike hematite crystals. It is no longer commercially mined.

TIGER'S-EYE: This is a translucent to opaque quartz with a silky luster and brown and gold silky stripes. (Technically, it's a quartz replacement of a type of asbestos called crocidolite.) Stones cut *en cabochon* with a gold linear reflection along the center are cat's-eyes because of the fibrous structure of the stone. South Africa, Australia, India and China are the most important sources of tiger's-eye. It sells for about $5–$70 per stone. A grayish-blue quartz with a similar cat's-eye effect is called **HAWK'S-EYE**. A unique brecciated type of tiger's eye with colors that shift from brown to blue to gold is found in Namibia and is sold under the name **PIETERSITE**.

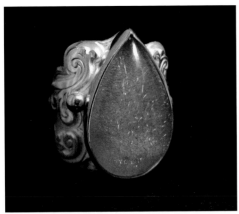

Fig. Am.8 Strawberry quartz. *Ring by Different Seasons Jewelry; photo by Jessica Dow.*

Fig. Am.9 Bicolor quartz. *Earrings and photo courtesy Mark Schneider Design.*

Fig. Am.10 Tiger's-eye. *Pendant: The Jeweler's Bench; photo: Skip Colflesh.*

Fig. Am.11 Smoky quartz. *Carving: Sherris Cottier Shank / Azad.*

Fig. Am.12 Rose quartz. *Ring by Zaffiro; photo by Elizabeth Gualtieri.*

Fig. Am.13 Aventurine. *Photo by Sindi Schloss of International Gemological Services.*

Am.14 Namibian pietersite. *Ring & photo courtesy John S. White.*

Chalcedony SiO_2—Silica (Cryptocrystalline quartz)

Bloodstone—a March birthstone; Sardonyx—an August birthstone

Designers love gem varieties of chalcedony (cal CED o nee). Its varied patterns and color combinations allow them to create attractive jewelry pieces that are unique. Chalcedony is affordable, durable and suitable for fine carving. Besides being used in jewelry, it's also fashioned into bowls, vases, figurines and other decorative articles.

Chalcedony is a confusing term because it has three different meanings. It can refer to all varieties of cryptocrystalline quartz (quartz composed of submicroscopic crystals). It can be a subcategory of cryptocrystalline quartz—the type whose crystal components look like twisted fibers rather than grains like those of many jaspers. And thirdly, "chalcedony" can indicate a plain white, gray or bluish gray chalcedony that is not agate, jasper or another sub-variety. Properties of chalcedony are listed below:

RI:1.53–1.54	**SG**: 2.55–2.69; some jasper 2.9	**Hardness**: 6.5–7	**Toughness**: Very good
Cleavage: None	**Crystal System**: Trigonal	**Pleochroism**: None	**Optic Character**: AGG

Reaction to Heat: The color may change depending on the cause of color.
Stability to Light: Usually stable, but irradiated stones or those dyed with organic dyes can fade.
Care Tips: Ultrasonics are usually safe if the stones are not dyed. Avoid strong heat and acids.
Treatments: Carnelian & tiger's-eye are usually heated; chrysoprase & jasper are occasionally heated; blue-green chalcedony and black onyx are sometimes irradiated; agate & tiger's-eye are often bleached, jasper is occasionally dyed, blue chalcedony, banded agate, carnelian and sard are often dyed, Black onyx is almost always dyed. Treatment information from: www.jtv.com/library/gemstone-chart.html.

Varieties & Trade Names

AGATE: Dealers tend to apply the term agate to any patterned chalcedony that is translucent or semi-translucent, as opposed to jasper, a variety that is usually opaque to the naked eye. In a more strict usage, agate is a chalcedony with curved or angular bands (layers) of color. The bands may be multicolored or similar in color and may alternate with bands of coarsely crystallized colorless quartz. Certain types of colorless or gray agates from Brazil and Madagascar are often stained (permanently dyed) red, black, green, blue or yellow with stable, inorganic chemicals. Other sources of agate include Mexico, Russia, India and the U.S.

Some white, gray or colorless chalcedony with inclusions is called agate. MOSS AGATE has moss-like green, brown, and/or red inclusions. DENDRITIC AGATE (LANDSCAPE AGATE) Has dark inclusions that resemble trees or ferns.

Agate formed in cavities may have a crystallized crust of tiny quartz crystals (e.g., geode). This agate is called DRUSY AGATE or DRUSY CHALCEDONY.

BLOODSTONE (HELIOTROPE): An opaque dark green chalcedony with orange or red spots, which some early Christians thought represented the blood of Jesus Christ. Bloodstone used to be prescribed as a cure for all types of bleeding. The injured or sick person would either wear it or place it over the affected area and the bleeding was supposed to stop. India is the main source of bloodstone. Retail prices range from about $5–$50 per stone in sizes from 3x5mm to 15x20mm.

CHALCEDONY: White, gray or bluish gray chalcedony. Some of the main deposits are in Brazil, Madagascar, India and the U.S. It retails for about $1–$30 per stone.

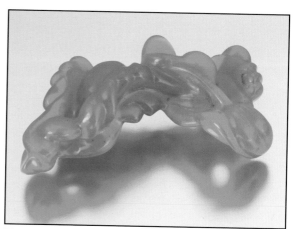

Fig. Ca.2 Chrysocolla chalcedony carved by Meg Berry. *Carving courtesy Pala International; photo by Mia Dixon.*

Fig. Ca.1 Dendritic agate. *Pendant by Patrick Murphy and Emily Chesick; photo by Corey Morse.*

Fig. Ca.3 Agatized dinosaur bone (gembone) inlay. *Belt buckle by Mark Anderson of Different Seasons Jewelry; photo by Jessica Dow.*

Fig. Ca.4 Cherry Creek jasper from mainland China and carnelian accents. *Earrings by Patrick Murphy & Emily Chesick; photo by Corey Morse.*

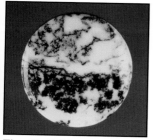

Fig. Ca.5 Moss agate from India. *Photo © Renée Newman.*

Fig. Ca.6 Bloodstone. *Photo © by Renée Newman.*

Ca.7 Carnelian. *Ring by Claudia Endler; photo by Barry Blau.*

BLUE CHALCEDONY: A popular bluish gray to blue to lavender stone found in Namibia, Malawi, Turkey, Mexico, Indonesia, British Columbia and the Western USA. Banded material is usually referred to as BLUE LACE AGATE.

CARNELIAN (CORNELIAN in the UK): Translucent orange or red chalcedony. Essentially all material sold as carnelian is heat-treated or dyed and heated chalcedony. Brownish red to brown chalcedony is called SARD. There's no distinct dividing line between sard and carnelian. Both varieties are found in Brazil and Uruguay. You can find them for sale for about $2–$40 per stone.

CHRYSOCOLLA CHALCEDONY: Greenish-blue chalcedony that is colored by copper and a small amount of the mineral chrysocolla. If it's even-colored and very translucent, trade members call it GEM CHRYSOCOLLA or GEM SILICA. Much of the best quality is found near Globe, Arizona. The finest material can retail from $200–$300/ct. Prices for semi-opaque mottled stones extend below $10/ct.

CHRYSOPRASE: Translucent light to medium-green chalcedony colored by nickel and somewhat resembling jade. It used to be the most prized chalcedony variety. Poland was an ancient source of chrysoprase and the sole source for hundreds of years. Today the most important deposits are in Queensland, Western Australia, Brazil, Tanzania and Kazakhstan. Chrysoprase retails for roughly $4–$100/ct.

FIRE AGATE: A gemstone that displays iridescent layers of color caused by oxides mixed with transparent chalcedony in botryoidal formation. Fire agate jewelry is especially suitable for men's jewelry because of its toughness and durability. You're most likely to find fire agate for sale in Arizona and Mexico, the areas where it's mined. Retail prices can range from $5-200/ct when properly cut and polished.

JASPER: An almost opaque, fine-grained chalcedony which is colored by foreign material. It's usually multicolored, spotted or striped but can be uniformly colored. The most common colors are red, brown, yellow, gray and green. Blue and black are not as prevalent. Jasper is found worldwide. Jasper with patterns reminiscent of desert landscapes is called PICTURE JASPER and is particularly popular in Western American jewelry. ORBICULAR JASPER contains spherical inclusions or zones like "ocean jasper" from Madagascar. MOOKAITE (MOUKAITE) is a purple and yellow Australian jasper. Jasper retails for about $5–$100 per cabochon and sometimes up to $250.

ONYX: Chalcedony composed of relatively straight, parallel layers of different colors. When the dark layers (bands) are brown or brownish red, it's often called SARDONYX. Layered onyx is ideal for cameos. It's produced when dense layers do not absorb dye and remain white while other more porous layers take on the dyes and end up blue, green, black, etc. BLACK ONYX is not really onyx. It's chalcedony that has been dyed completely black. It's priced at about $1–$30 per piece retail. Black onyx with sandblasted designs on it retails for up to $200 per piece.

PETRIFIED WOOD: (Fossilized Wood, Agatized Wood): Wood that has been replaced by chalcedony. Petrification can occur when trees are covered with fine sedimentary rock rich in volcanic ash shortly after their death. The wood does not turn into stone. It is just gradually replaced by silica which preserves the shape, color and structural elements of the wood. The most famous occurrence of petrified wood is at the Petrified Forest National Park in Arizona. Petrified wood can be agate, jasper or opal. Shells, leaves and bones can also undergo petrification. Dinosaur bone petrified with agate is called AGATIZED DINOSAUR BONE or DINOSAUR GEMBONE. See *Exotic Gems: Volumes 2 & 3* by Renée Newman for in-depth information on gembone, fire agate & blue chalcedony.

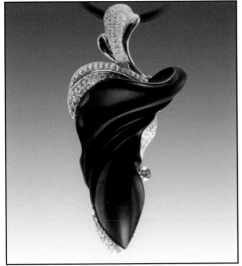

Fig. Ca.8 Black onyx carved by Steve Walters. *Pendant by Sugarman-Frantz Designs; photo by Michael Sugarman.*

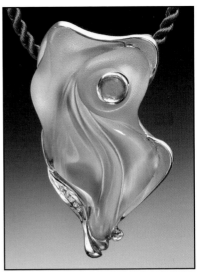

Fig. Ca.9 Blue chalcedony carved by Steve Walters. *Pendant by Fred & Kate Pearce; photo by Ralph Gabriner.*

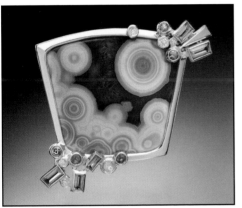

Fig. Ca.10 Ocean jasper. *Pendant by Fred & Kate Pearce; photo by Ralph Gabriner.*

Fig. Ca.11 Fire agate. *Ring: Fire Agate Art Studio; photo by Ryszard Krukowski.*

Fig. Ca.12 Chrysoprase. *Jewelry by Different Seasons Jewelry; photo by Jessica Dow.*

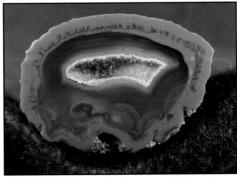

Fig. Ca.13 Jurassic yellow cat petrified redwood from Moab, Utah. *Photo by Larry Walker.*

Chrysoberyl (Alexandrite, Cat's Eye) $BeAl_2O_4$—Beryllium aluminum
oxide, Alexandrite—a June birthstone; Cat's-eye—18th wedding anniversary

Alexandrite and cat's-eye look very different, yet they are the same mineral—chrysoberyl. A third, less expensive type of chrysoberyl is transparent, shows no optical effects and ranges in color from green, to yellow to brown. Thanks to their good hardness and durability, all types of chrysoberyl are well-suited for jewelry use. Today, Brazil and Sri Lanka are the most important sources of chrysoberyls. Deposits are also found in Russia, Tanzania, India, Zimbabwe, Madagascar and Myanmar (Burma). Listed below are the physical and optical characteristics of chrysoberyl:

RI: 1.74–1.76	SG: 3.64–3.80	Hardness: 8.5	Toughness: Good to excellent
Cleavage: Indistinct or none		DR, biaxial positive	**Crystal System**: Orthorhombic
Pleochroism: Strong trichroism in alexandrite, none in cat's-eye, weak to moderate in transparent yellow, green and brown varieties			
Care Tips: Ultrasonics & steamers are safe if stone has no fractures. Stable to heat & light; no reaction to chemicals; overall, a durable natural gemstone with excellent wearability.			
Treatments: Occasionally heated. Occasionally fractures may be masked with fillers.			

ALEXANDRITE: This gem was first discovered in the Ural Mountains of Russia in the early 1830's. The name "alexandrite" was officially accepted in 1842 in honor of Tzar Alexander II. In its finest qualities, alexandrite looks bluish green in sunlight and purplish-red to purple in incandescent light (light bulbs). Don't expect to find natural alexandrite in your local jewelry store—it's very rare. When you do see it for sale, the colors are likely to be a grayish blue-green and brownish purple or lavender. Synthetic alexandrite and synthetic alexandrite-like sapphire or spinel are readily available. Natural alexandrites in the 1-3 ct range that show a noticeable change of color can retail from $3000–$20,000/ct. Larger top-quality stones can cost as much as $50,000/ct. The distinctness of the color change and the color intensity are the most important price factors, but size and clarity also affect the cost.

CAT'S-EYE: Treasured for centuries in the Orient, cat's-eye became popular in Europe in the late 19th century when the Duke of Connaught gave a cat's-eye engagement ring to Princess Louise Margaret of Prussia. Today, cat's-eye is used mostly in men's jewelry. Other minerals such as quartz, tourmaline and beryl may also display a cat's-eye (a moving stripe of reflected light across a cabochon), but chrysoberyl cat's-eye is the most prized and usually has the sharpest eye. The unmodified term **cat's-eye** means chrysoberyl cat's-eye. Other cat's-eye stones must indicate the mineral, as for example cat's-eye quartz or quartz cat's-eye. A brownish yellow similar to the color of honey is the most valued color, but greenish-yellow stones can also be very expensive. In the finest qualities, cat's-eye can retail for more than $10,000/ct. Stones with fuzzy, non-sharp eyes, dull colors and eye-visible inclusions can sell for less than $200/ct. Cat's-eye can also display a color change. Alexandrite cat's-eyes, however, are quite rare.

YELLOW, GREEN or BROWN (transparent) **CHRYSOBERYL**: Attractive and durable, high-quality yellow or green chrysoberyl retails for about $300–$1500/ct, depending on size. Unfortunately, you won't find it in many jewelry stores, although it is becoming more available. For more detailed information on chrysoberyl, cat's-eye and alexandrite, consult *Exotic Gems, Volume 2* by Renée Newman.

Fig. Cr.1 An exceptional 2.88-carat natural alexandrite with no inclusions. *Ring and photo courtesy Mark Henry Jewelry.*

Fig. Cr.2 An alexandrite (0.85 ct) flanked by matching specialty-cut kite-shaped alexandrites. *Ring and photo courtesy Mark Henry Jewelry.*

Fig. Cr.3 Brazilian alexandrite (3.03 cts) (daylight) from Mayer & Watt. *Photo: Geoffrey Watt.*

Fig. Cr.4 Same alexandrite (incandescent). *Mayer & Watt; photo by Geoffrey D. Watt.*

Fig. Cr.5 Cat's-eye (10 cts). *Gent's ring from Lang Antiques, San Francisco; photo: Cole Bybee.*

Fig. Cr.6 Chrysoberyl. *Ring by Linda Quinn Designs; photo by Chris Rockafellow.*

Emerald & Other Beryls $Be_3Al_2(SiO_3)_6$—Beryllium aluminum silicate

Emerald—May birthstone; aquamarine—March birthstone
Emerald—20th & 35th anniversaries

In its pure form, beryl is colorless. But thanks to the presence of impurities, this mineral can be blue, green, pink, red, yellow or orange. If, for example, traces of chromium and/or vanadium are present, the result may be an emerald. A trace of iron can turn the beryl into aquamarine, whereas a bit of manganese adds a pink or orange color to the stone. Of all the beryls, emerald is the most highly valued and has the longest history. Some evidence indicates that emerald deposits in Egypt may have been exploited as early as 3500 BC. However, most of the Egyptian emeralds were pale, drab and heavily flawed. It wasn't until the 1500's, when the Spanish invaded the Americas, that Europeans realized how beautiful an emerald could be because vast quantities of Colombian emeralds were brought to Europe by the conquistadors.

Aquamarine and yellow beryl have also had a long history, but it's hard to determine when they were first used as ornamental stones. The orange, pink and red beryls have only been recognized as gems since the early 1900's. Listed below are the physical and optical properties of the beryl family.

RI: 1.57–1.60	**SG**: 2.67–2.80	**Hardness**: 7.5–8	**Crystal System**: Hexagonal	
Toughness: Poor to good depending on clarity			**Optic character**: DR, uniaxial neg	
Pleochroism: Emerald, moderate to strong yellowish-green & bluish-green; weak to moderate dichroism in the other beryls			**Cleavage**: Rare and indistinct in one direction	
Reaction to Heat: In emerald, it may cause fracturing or complete breakage; Maxixe and Maxixe-type beryl (see description below) fade quickly at 100^0 C or higher.				
Stability to Light: Stable, except for Maxixe and Maxixe-type beryl. There can also be fading in orange beryl or in emeralds treated with green oil. In addition, orange beryl may change to pink.				
Reaction to Chemicals: Resists all acids except hydrofluoric; solvents such as acetone and alcohol may drive out fracture fillings in emerald.				
Care tips: Clean emeralds with a damp cloth or spray with window cleaner & wipe dry. Don't soak emeralds in cleaning solutions because they can dissolve fillers. Ultrasonics are usually safe for beryls of good clarity.				
Treatments: Assume that emeralds & red beryl have been fracture filled unless otherwise stated. Pink beryl and aquamarine are usually heated; yellow beryl is usually irradiated; emeralds are sometimes dyed.				

Varieties & Trade Names

EMERALD: The definition of an emerald varies depending on the user. At gem shows and in stores, any beryl that looks more or less green is typically labeled as an emerald. Some emerald dealers feel that light green stones should be called "green beryl" and that the term "emerald" should be reserved for darker stones. European gemologists tend to believe true emeralds must be colored by chromium, whereas American gemologists think stones colored by vanadium are also emeralds. The definition of "emerald" is irrelevant when it comes to pricing. If a one-carat beryl has a saturated green color and is transparent and eye-clean, it can be worth more than $10,000 retail. Top quality, 6-carat emeralds can retail for over $20,000/ct. Low-grade semiopaque emerald or beryl can sell for as little as $10/ct. Emeralds which have a six-rayed star pattern formed by black inclusions are called **trapiche emeralds**.

Fig. Em.1 Columbian emeralds. *Earrings by Hubert; photo by Diamond Graphics.*

Fig. Em.2 Green and blue beryl (aquamarine). *Earrings: Hubert; photo: Diamond Graphics.*

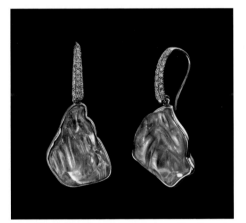

Fig. Em.3 Freeform aquamarine. *Earrings by Hubert; photo by Diamond Graphics.*

Fig. Em.4 Morganite. *Earrings by Cynthia Renée Inc; photo: John Parrish.*

Fig. Em.5 Red beryl (2.39 ct, untreated). *Carving & photo by Glenn Lehrer.*

Fig. Em.6 Golden beryl from Brazil (11.35 cts). *Cut by John Dyer; photo by Lydia Dyer.*

It's common for an emerald to have inclusions and fractures, especially if it has a deep green color. Nevertheless, clarity and transparency play a major role in emerald pricing. Emeralds are routinely treated with oil, wax or epoxy-like substances to hide fractures and improve transparency. This is considered an acceptable trade practice as long as it is disclosed. Some fillers are more stable than others, but it's usually not possible for salespeople to know exactly what an emerald has been filled with. Lab documents, however, can provide you with information on the extent and type of filling. Reputable jewelers will stand behind their emeralds, and many will agree to treat the stones again if necessary.

Colombia is the most important source of top-grade emerald. High-quality emerald is also found in Zambia, Zimbabwe, Brazil and Pakistan, but not in the same quantities as in Colombia. Other deposits include Russia, Afghanistan, India and North Carolina.

GREEN BERYL: There is no agreed-upon criterion in the trade for distinguishing between green beryl and emerald. Likewise, there is no clear dividing line between green beryl and aquamarine.

AQUAMARINE: The name "aquamarine" means "sea water" in Latin, alluding to its color. Most natural-color aquamarine is light bluish-green. Prior to the 1900's, this was the preferred color for aquamarine but today it's routinely heat-treated to remove any green component, thereby producing a permanently-colored blue stone. The more intense the blue color, the more valuable the stone. Aquamarines usually have a high transparency and clarity, even under magnification. They're also very durable and their color is evenly distributed. Fine quality stones above a carat retail for about $700 to $2,300/ct. Brazil is the most important producer of aquamarine. Madagascar, Mozambique, Ukraine, Nigeria, Pakistan and Zambia are other major sources.

MAXIXE BERYL: This beryl has a medium to dark color resembling blue sapphire. It was named after the mine in Brazil where it was discovered around 1917. Since then, a similar stone has appeared on the market called Maxixe-type beryl. It is produced by irradiating pale pink or colorless beryl. Maxixe and Maxixe-type beryls are rare and they fade when exposed to light.

HELIODOR (YELLOW BERYL): Found in Madagascar, Brazil, Russia, Namibia and the U.S., this beryl is not uncommon. It's also been called golden beryl. In sizes above a carat, it retails for about $100–$600 ct.

MORGANITE (PINK or ORANGE BERYL): Morganite was named after the famous financier J. P. Morgan. The first morganite to be described was a pale pink variety found in California. Some of the finest, most intensely-colored morganite is found in Madagascar. Brazil is another important source, but the colors of Brazilian material are usually lighter even though the crystals are much larger. Morganite is commonly heat-treated to intensify the color. Fine quality stones retail for about $200–$1,000 ct.

RED BERYL (BIXBITE): This valuable beryl was discovered in Utah in 1906. Red beryl is sometimes erroneously called red emerald. Due to its rarity, it remains a collector gem. The color of red beryl is due to trace amounts of manganese.

GOSHENITE (COLORLESS BERYL): Goshenite is named after Goshen, Massachusetts, a source of colorless beryl. It has been used to imitate diamond or emerald by placing silver or green colored metal foil behind it in a closed back setting. Goshenite is not common.

CAT'S-EYE BERYL: Chatoyancy is most likely to occur in aquamarine and morganite. However, cat's-eye emerald and cat's-eye yellow beryl also exist. These are collector stones.

Fig. Em.7 Yellow beryl. *Earrings © Eve Alfillé; photo by Matthew Arden.*

Fig. Em.8 Carved emerald. *Ring by Zaffiro; photo by Elizabeth Gualtieri.*

Fig. Em.9 Morganite. *Necklace and photo by Loretta Castoro.*

Fig. Em.10 Morganite. *Earrings and photo by Loretta Castoro.*

Fig. Em.11 Aquamarine. *Ring and photo courtesy Suna Bros.*

Fig. Em.12 Trapiche emerald. *Mayer & Watt / Geoffrey Watt.*

Fig.Em.13 Maxixe-type beryl. *Photo by Robert Weldon.*

Fig. Em.14 Red beryl. *Bracelet by Cynthia Renée, Inc; photo by Harold & Erica Van Pelt.*

Garnet (a group of mineral species)
January birthstone and 2nd wedding anniversary stone

Friendship—this is what the garnet represents. According to legend, adorning yourself with garnets will improve your personal relationships and protect you from harm. These benefits are doubled if your birthday is in January. Traditionally, people have thought that garnets are only red, but they can also be green, yellow, orange, brown, pink or purple and even black.

The word "garnet" comes from the Latin *granatum* meaning "seedlike." Garnet crystals in rock reminded early scientists of the shape and color of pomegranate seeds.

Historical accounts and findings suggest that garnet beads and inlaid jewelry were worn in Egypt as early as 3100 BC. Tracing the history of gemstones is difficult because they were often misidentified. It's certain, however, that during the 18th and 19th centuries, garnets were popular in Europe. The bourgeoisie would buy these stones while vacationing in the hot springs of Bohemia, Czechoslovakia, and take them home as souvenirs and good luck charms. Until the late 1800's, Bohemia was the world's major source of pyrope (a garnet species).

Below is a chart which lists various members of the garnet group. Much of the data is from *Gems* by Robert Webster and the *GIA Gem Identification Lab Manual*. Keep in mind that garnets are almost always a mixture of different garnet species and have varying properties. The species name refers to the main component of a garnet. Use this table as a general guide only; the RI, SG and hardness values may be higher or lower than indicated, and there can be a wide variation of color within a given species. One garnet species, uvarovite, was not included because it's usually too small to be cut into gemstones. However, a drusy form has been on the market since the late 1990's.

Species	Varieties	Basic Color	RI	SG	Hardness
Andradite	Demantoid Topazolite Melanite	Green Yellow / orange Black	1.88–1.89	3.81–3.87	6.5–7
Spessartine	 Little Three Mine Mandarin garnet	Orange or orange-red Orange Orange	1.78 – 1.81	4.12–4.20	7–7.5
Almandine (if pure) Almandine		Purple to red Purple to red	1.83 1.78–1.83	4.25 3.80–4.25	7.5 7.25
Pyrope-almandine	Rhodolite	Purple-red / pink	1.75–1.78	3.80–3.95	7.25
Pyrope Pyrope (if pure)		Red Red	1.73–1.75 1.71	3.65–3.80 3.51	7.25 7.25
Grossular-andradite	Mali garnet	Green or yellow	1.75–1.78	3.64–3.68	6.75–7
Pyrope-spessartine	Color change & Malaia garnet	Variable Orange / pink-orange	1.74–1.78	3.78–3.85	7.25
Grossular	Hessonite Tsavorite Translucent green Translucent white Translucent pink	Orange or yellow Green Green White Pink	1.74–1.76 1.74–1.76 1.72–1.73 1.72–1.73 1.70–1.73	3.59–3.65 3.57–3.64 3.42–3.50 3.45–3.50 3.35–3.41	7.25 7.25 7 7 7

Fig. G.1 Spessartine (14.12 cts). *Ring by Hubert; photo by Diamond Graphics.*

Fig. G.2 Mint garnet (grossular). *Cut by J. L. White Fine Gemstones.; photo by Jeff White.*

Fig. G.3 Tsavorite (10.63 cts). *Ring by Cynthia Renée Inc; photo by Mogadham.*

Fig. G.4 Rhodolite from the Umba River area of Tanzania (umbalite). *Pala Intl / Mia Dixon.*

Fig. G.5 Color-change garnet from Kenya. *Cut by Lisa Elser; photo by C. Tom Schlegel.*

Fig.G.6 Spessartine (7.86 cts). *Ring and photo courtesy Omi Privé.*

Fig. G.7 Garnet color suite. *Gemstones and photo courtesy John S. White.*

Jewelers often identify lower-priced garnets as simply garnets. It's not worth the time and money to test the stones and determine their species. Properties shared by the various garnets are listed below.

Crystal System: Cubic (isometric)	Cleavage: None, but may have indistinct parting
Toughness: Fair to good	Optic Char: Singly refractive, anomalous double refraction
Treatments: Normally none, but may be heated (particularly demantoid), fracture filling is possible.	
Care Tips: Ultrasonics are usually safe with good-clarity stones; avoid sudden temperature changes.	

Species, Varieties & Trade Names

ANDRADITE ($Ca_3Fe_2(SiO_4)_3$): The best known andradite variety is DEMANTOID, which was discovered in the mid 19th century in the Ural Mountains of Russia. It resembles an emerald with added brilliance and fire. Its fire (dispersion) is even greater than that of diamonds. The name "demantoid" comes from the Old German word *demant* meaning diamond-like. Much Victorian gemstone jewelry made between 1885 and 1915 featured demantoid.

Good demantoid is rare and typically weighs less than a carat. Discoveries in Madagascar and Namibia have made it more available. Some demantoid is also mined in Italy, Pakistan and the Iran-Afghanistan border area. Asbestos-fiber inclusions resembling horsetails are considered a positive feature in demantoid. Their presence strongly suggests the stones are from the historic Russian Urals region. Demantoid is the most expensive garnet. Stones below 0.50 carat can retail for as much as $1200/ct. Extra fine demantoids above 10 carats, have *wholesaled* for more than $20,000/ct.

The opaque black variety of andradite, MELANITE, has been used in mourning jewelry. The crystals of TOPAZOLITE, a yellow to brown variety, are rare and typically small.

SPESSARTINE or SPESSARTITE ($Mn_3Al_2(SiO_4)_3$): This species ranges from yellowish orange to brownish orange or orangish red and is colored by manganese. The most valued color is orange with red overtones. Sources include Afghanistan, Brazil, California, Madagascar, Mozambique, Myanmar, Namibia, Nigeria, Pakistan, Sri Lanka and Tanzania. One place that's particularly noted for high-quality spessartine is the Little Three Mine in California. Spessartine mined in Namibia is usually called MANDARIN GARNET and sells for premium prices. Tanzania is also a major producer of high quality spessartine. Retail prices of top-grade material can be as high as $2500/ct. However, you can find good spessartines for between $100–$1000/ct.

ALMANDINE or ALMANDITE ($Fe_3Al_2(SiO_4)_3$): Much of the material that is sold as almandine is low-priced pyrope (garnet composed mostly of pyrope with some almandine and grossular). This leads people to believe that gem almandine is more plentiful than it actually is. Opinions differ as to how almandine should be defined. At the very least, the chief component should be almandine. But trade members disagree on how much almandine should be present and what its properties should be. According to noted gemologist Robert Webster (*Gems*, p. 174), the bottom limits for the refractive index and specific gravity of almandine are 1.78 and 3.95. However, these figures are arbitrary. Almandines of high purity are rare and typically have a purplish or reddish color. Sources include Sri Lanka, India, Brazil, Australia, Tanzania, Madagascar and the U.S. Star and cat's eye almandine is found in Idaho, India and Sri Lanka. The star garnets usually have four rays but six rays may occasionally be seen.

Fig. G.8 Nigerian spessartine (center 21.8 cts), side stones (5.33 ct). *Ring by Cynthia Renée, Inc; photo by JB photo.*

Fig. G.9 Rhodolites and tsavorites. *Earring from Sarosi by Timeless Gems; photo by Diamond Graphics.*

Fig. G.10 Melanite garnet and rutilated quartz. *Ring © Eve J. Alfillé; photo by Matthew Arden.*

Fig.G.11 Russian demantoid (3.51 cts). *Pala Intl. / Mia Dixon.*

Fig. G.12 Mandarin garnet. *Ring and photo courtesy Suna Bros.*

Fig. G.13 Anthill pyrope garnet. *Ring and photo courtesy Sami's Fine Jewelry.*

Fig.G.14 Mali garnet (1.69 cts). *Cut by John Dyer & Co; photo by Priscilla Dyer.*

Fig. G.15 Malaya garnet (6.58 cts). *Cut and photographed by Clay Zava of Zava Mastercuts.*

PYROPE-ALMANDINE: This is usually called RHODOLITE and was discovered in 1882 in North Carolina. Those deposits have been depleted, but since then it has been found in Africa, Brazil, India and Sri Lanka. Tanzania is the major commercial source. The name of this purplish-red garnet comes from the Greek *rhodo* (rose) and *lithos* (stone). Rhodolites often retail for about $10–$400/ct. Top-quality stones are clean, very transparent and saturated in color but not dark.

PYROPE (PIE rope) ($Mg_3Al_2(SiO_4)_3$): This garnet's name is derived from the Greek *pyropos* meaning "fire-like," alluding to its deep red color. Pyrope is found throughout the world, with some of the best quality coming from the diamond mines of South Africa. As a result, it has sometimes been referred to as "cape ruby." "Arizona ruby" is a misnomer for pyrope from Arizona. Pyrope colored by chromium is called CHROME PYROPE or ANTHILL GARNET if it is found in anthills. The redder the stone, the more valuable it is.

GROSSULAR-ANDRADITE: Since 1995 this has been marketed as MALI GARNET or GRANDITE. It's found in western Africa in the Republic of Mali and can be various shades of green, yellow or brown. Stones generally retail for about $150–$1500/ct.

PYROPE-SPESSARTINE: One distinctive orange variety is called MALAIA or MALAYA and it may be reddish, pinkish or yellowish. It was found along the Tanzania and Kenyan border in the search for rhodolite, a purplish-red garnet coveted in Japan. Initially considered a reject garnet, it's now in high demand. Pinkish orange and orange with overtones of red are the most valued colors. "Malaia" is the Swahili word for "outcast" or "prostitute."

COLOR-CHANGE GARNET is found in many different colors and displays a variation of color behavior. For example, it may be blue or green in daylight and reddish, purple, orange or brown in incandescent light. Color-change garnet consists mainly of pyrope-spessartine with some grossular. It's found in Madagascar, Tanzania, Kenya, Sri Lanka, Russia and some parts of the U.S.A. Because of its rarity, it may retail for more than $3000/ct in top qualities with a distinct color change.

GROSSULAR or **GROSSULARITE** ($Ca_3Al_2(SiO_4)_3$): The most valued variety of this species is TSAVORITE (also TSAVOLITE), a transparent green garnet. It was discovered in Tanzania in 1968. Later it was also found in Kenya, and promoters from Tiffany & Co. named it after the country's Tsavo National Park. Tsavorite is found in almost all shades of green but tends to be yellowish-green. Stones with a high clarity and color resembling that of fine emeralds can retail for more than $8000/ct in sizes above three carats. Retail prices of smaller commercial quality stones can fall below$500/ct. Grossular that is light green and transparent is typically called green grossular or MINT GARNET.

HESSONITE is a much less expensive variety of grossular that is sometimes called **cinnamon stone**. The colors are often brownish and can be red, orange, yellow or colorless. When viewed under magnification, hessonite typically has a granular "heat wave" appearance. There are hessonite deposits in Sri Lanka, Tanzania, Kenya, Mexico, the U.S., Canada, Madagascar, Russia and Brazil. Retail prices may range from about $25–$500/ct depending on size, quality and source.

Translucent and semiopaque grossular is used for beads, cabochons and carvings. The green material (technically named HYDROGROSSULAR) is sometimes called **Transvaal jade**, after its main source in South Africa. It has also been found in the USSR, Hungary and Italy. Small black inclusions (black specks) are a characteristic of this green grossular. Translucent pink grossular, mixed in white marble, is found mainly in Mexico and is sometimes called **rosolite**, after its color.

Iolite (Cordierite species) $Mg_2Al_4Si_5O_{18}$—a complex silicate of magnesium and aluminum, 21st wedding anniversary stone

Before the 1980's, iolite was mainly considered a collector's stone because so little of it was being sold. Today, it is more readily available, and it is sometimes used as a sapphire or tanzanite substitute because of its blue-violet color and lower price. Iolite of high quality retails for less than $250/ ct. Very dark and flawed stones sell for much less.

Mineralogists call the stone **cordierite**, a name given to the mineral in honor of French geologist Pierre Cordier, the founder of the French Geological Society. The name iolite was derived from the Greek word for violet, *ios*. Some people have referred to iolite as **water sapphire** because it resembles sapphire face-up and it looks clear or watery from the side. This effect is due to the strong trichroism of iolite. In one direction the crystal typically appears dark blue or violet; in another it is colorless, gray or yellowish; and in a third direction it is light blue or violet.

Iolite has also been referred to as the "Viking's compass." On cloudy days, the Vikings were able to locate the position of the sun by looking through thin colorless slices of iolite. The stone acted as a light polarizer and canceled out haze and mist.

The Vikings probably got their iolite from Greenland or Norway, but today most of it comes from India, Sri Lanka, Tanzania and Brazil. Additional sources include Myanmar, Madagascar, Zimbabwe and Namibia. The physical and optical properties of iolite are listed below.

RI: 1.53–1.58	**SG**: 2.56–2.66	**Hardness**: 7–7.5	**Crystal System**: Orthorhombic
Toughness: fair	**Trichroism**: strong	**Optic Character**: DR, biaxial negative	
Treatments: normally not treated		**Cleavage**: Distinct in one direction	
Care tips: Ultrasonics are risky; avoid acids and sudden temperature changes.			

Fig. I.1 Iolite. *Earrings © by Eve J. Alfillé; photo by Matthew Arden.*

Fig. I.2 Iolite, a gem that looks blue face-up and colorless from the side. *Photo by Henry A. Hänni © SSEF.*

Right: Fig. I.3 Iolite. *Carving by Sherris Cottier Shank; photo from Gemscapes.*

Jade   (Jadeite & Nephrite)   12th wedding anniversary stone

...jade is a possession to be cherished by anyone who can find it or buy it or steal it. Chinese women ask for jade ornaments for their hair, and old men keep in their closed palms a piece of cool jade, so smooth that it seems soft to the touch. Rich men buy jades instead of putting their money in banks, for jade grows more beautiful with age.   Pearl S. Buck, *My Several Worlds*

No other natural stone is as resistant to breakage and chipping as jade. This inherent toughness made it a superior weapon and tool for early man. To him it meant survival, and its colors were reminiscent of nature. As a result, jade became known as a gift from heaven. It was even more esteemed than diamonds or gold by some civilizations in Asia, Central America and the South Pacific. Jade represented everything that is positive—beauty, purity, resilience, loyalty, nobility, perfection, and immortality. Because of its historical significance and the virtues that it represents, the Chinese used it for their 2008 Beijing Olympic medals. The jade symbolized Chinese culture and expressed the Olympic spirit of unification and friendship. Today jade is worn by millions of Asians for good luck and health, and it is given to celebrate all-important occasions in life, such as births, marriages, anniversaries and business agreements.

The English term "jade" originated from the Spanish phrase *piedra de ijada* (loin stone), perhaps because the Spanish thought jade could protect against and cure loin ailments. In translation from Spanish to French, *piedra de ijada* was misprinted as *pierre le jade*. The translation into Latin was *lapis nephrictus,* which led the German geologist Abraham G. Werner to name jade "**nephrite**" in 1780. It wasn't until 1863 that the French chemist Augustine Damour chemically analyzed a Burmese jade carving and discovered that it was different from Chinese nephrite. He called the Burmese material "**jadeite**." In 1881, it was discovered that Burmese jade and jade from Central America were both composed of the mineral jadeite.

Jadeite and nephrite are both rocks —masses of tightly interlocking crystals, rather than single crystals like most gems. However, they have different chemical compositions and properties. Jadeite is a little harder and denser and as a result, it can take a higher polish than nephrite. Neither stone is very hard, compared to diamond, ruby and sapphire. However, both jades are exceptionally tough—highly resistant to breakage and chipping. Nephrite, however, is slightly tougher, due to its intergrown, fiberlike crystal components. Jadeite is made up of crystals which tend to be more granular and coarse-grained. Individual crystals are sometimes visible without magnification.

Most **jadeite** is more valuable and rare than nephrite. Myanmar (Burma) has been the main source of jadeite since the late 18th century, when China began to import it from there. Prior to that time, Guatemalan jadeite had been used extensively in Central America by Indians such as the Aztecs and the Mayas. Some jadeite is also mined in Russia, Japan and California; but the finest quality comes from Myanmar. When it has a high transparency and a strong emerald-green color, it is called **Imperial jade**. Jadeite is found in a variety of colors—lavender, white, gray, yellow, orange, brownish-red, black, colorless and many shades of green. Today, jadeite is usually the jade chosen for fine jewelry. Its intrinsic value is generally the basis for its price. Nephrite, on the other hand, is mainly valued for its antiquity, provenance and carving excellence.

Nephrite is plentiful and much of it is grayish green—typically forest green or olive green. It can also be white, gray, black, blue, yellow, orange or beige. The oldest known source of nephrite is Xinjiang Province in China (formerly Eastern Turkestan). For centuries, this is where China got its jade. The nephrite found in Xinjiang tends to be light in color.

Fig. J.1 Carved Burmese jadeite. *Earrings & photo courtesy Mason-Kay.*

Fig. J.2–4 Left to right: Nephrite jade from China, Kutcho Creek, British Columbia and Alaska. *Pendants carved and photographed by Deborah Wilson.*

Fig. J.5 Burmese jadeite. *Bracelets from Jade by Nikolai; photo by Nikolai Tsang.*

Fig. J.6 Burmese black jadeite. *Watch by Jade by Nikolai; photo by Nikolai Tsang.*

Fig. J.7 Burmese orange-red jadeite. *Ring and photo courtesy Mason-Kay.*

Fig. J.8 Blue jadeite from Guatemala. *Carving and photo by Glenn Lehrer.*

Although nephrite is usually thought of as an oriental stone, it has also been mined and carved in ceremonial fashion by other cultures throughout history—notably the Maoris of New Zealand, where it is found. Nephrite is also found in British Columbia, Siberia, China, Taiwan, Wyoming, California, Alaska, Washington state, the Yukon, South Korea, Australia, Japan and Switzerland. The chemical composition and properties of nephrite and jadeite can be compared by referring to the two charts below:

Jadeite NaAl(Si$_2$O$_6$)—Sodium aluminum silicate			
RI: 1.65–1.68	**SG:** 3.30–3.40	**Hardness:** 6.5–7	**Toughness:** Exceptional
Crystal System: Monoclinic		**Optic Character:** AGG (DR) biaxial positive	
Care Tips: Clean in soapy water. Ultrasonics can damage wax coating. Avoid acids and high heat.			
Treatments: Often bleached & filled with polymers and/or dyed. Sometimes heated; usually waxed.			

Nephrite Ca$_2$(Mg,Fe)$_5$(Si$_4$O$_{11}$)$_2$(OH)$_2$—Calcium magnesium iron silicate			
RI: 1.60–1.63	**SG:** 2.90–3.05	**Hardness** 6–6.5	**Toughness:** Exceptional, better than jadeite
Crystal System: Monoclinic		**Optic Character:** AGG (DR) biaxial positive	
Care Tips: Clean in soapy water. Ultrasonics can damage wax coating. Avoid acids and high heat			
Treatments: Often not treated, except for waxing. Sometimes dyed or heated.			

Evaluation of Jade

COLOR: An intense green with a medium to medium-dark tone is the most valued. As the color becomes lighter, darker, more grayish or brownish or yellowish, the value decreases. For jadeite, lavender or colorless are the next most valued, followed by black, red or yellow and white. Pure white is the most valued color for nephrite. White nephrite from Hotan (aka Hetian) in northwest China commands premium prices.

COLOR UNIFORMITY: In top quality jade, the color is uniform throughout the stone. The more uneven or blotchy the color is, the lower the value. Multicolored jade, however, can be very expensive if the colors are intense and distinct. The most desired color combinations are green and lavender, orange and green, or white with strong green (**moss-in-snow** jade). Uneven coloring can create interesting patterns.

TRANSPARENCY: The best jade is either near transparent or semitransparent. It's often described in the trade with terms such as **"glassy" jade, ice (icy) jade** or **water jade**. As the transparency of jade decreases, so does its value, with semiopaque jade being worth the least. Many jade dealers use the term **translucency** instead of "transparency." For the sake of consistency, this book uses the term "transparency" when categorizing the degree to which light passes through gems.

CLARITY: Fine jade is free of flaws such as cracks, included foreign material, cloudy areas, streaks and spots which reduce beauty or durability. The number, size, color, position and nature of flaws determines the clarity of a stone. Fractures that break the surface or that are visible internally are particularly detrimental to the value of jade.

Fig. J.9 Semitransparent imperial jadeite. *Burma jadeite cab courtesy Mason-Kay; photo © Renée Newman.*

Fig. J.10 Left: semitransparent jadeite. Right: translucent jadeite. Both stones are entirely natural. *Burma jade courtesy Mason-Kay; photo © Renée Newman.*

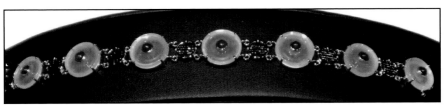

Fig. J.11 Ice jade. *Burmese jadeite bracelet from Mason-Kay; photo © Renée Newman.*

Fig. J.12 Translucent Burma jadeite. *Carving from Jade by Nikolai; photo: Nikolai Tsang.*

Fig. J.13 Semitransparent Burma jadeite. *Carving from Jade by Nikolai; photo by Nikolai Tsang.*

Fig. J.14 Yukon nephrite jade. *Pendant carved and photographed by Georg Schmerholz.*

Fig. J.15 Carved Burmese jadeite. *Pendant by Katy Briscoe; photo by Kennon Evett.*

TEXTURE: Jade can have a texture that ranges from fine to coarse. That's because it is composed of intergrown crystals. The finer and more tightly interwoven the crystal components are, the better the jade.

SHAPE: The best quality jade is cut into cabochons. Ovals and rounds normally sell for more than rectangular, marquise and pear shapes. Smooth uncarved pieces are more valuable than carved ones. Carving allows the removal of flaws from inferior material.

SIZE: Since large, fine quality jadeite is rare, size does play a role in increasing its value. The thickness of good jadeite is also important. If a jadeite cabochon is thinner than 2mm or smaller than 8 x 6 mm, there can be a considerable deduction in its per-carat value.

CUT QUALITY AND POLISH: Moderately thick cabochons tend to be more valued than flat or very high domed ones. Symmetrical cabochons with balanced proportions and no irregular flat spots are the most desired. The more brilliant the polish and the smoother the surface, the better the stone. Every scratch, sharp angle and rough surface should be removed during the polishing process. When stones lose their luster and become scratched, they can be repolished.

Texture and polish are related because fine-textured stones can take a higher polish than those with a coarse texture. Hardness is also important. Since nephrite is a little softer, it normally does not take as high a polish as jadeite.

Jade Treatments

WAXING: This treatment is considered acceptable in the trade. It's commonly done after the final polish to improve luster and hide pits and cracks. The stone is soaked in a colorless molten wax and then buffed to achieve a good shine. Heat and strong solvents will undo this treatment. Material which has received only a superficial waxing is often called **"A" jade** in the trade.

DYEING: This is done to add green or lavender color to white or light-colored jade. The stone is heated to open up the "pores" and then dye is forced into it often with high pressure. Blueberry juice is a common dye for lavender jade. It looks good at first but it can fade in sunlight. Gemologists use a microscope and spectrometers to detect dyes. Dyed jade is called **"C" Jade**.

HEATING: Dark green nephrite may be treated by this method to lighten its color. Jade containing yellow or brown inclusions in the rind may turn brown or red when heated. "Antique jade" articles are sometimes made from modern jade and aged artificially by heat treatment to simulate the oxidation found on some natural jade.

BLEACHING AND POLYMER IMPREGNATION: This treatment removes impurities and brown from jade, making white colors whiter and green colors brighter. The jade is first soaked and bleached in chemicals. Microscopic tunnels are created as silica is removed during the process. Then the bleached jade is impregnated with a synthetic material to fill these tunnels. The resulting material is called **"B" jade**. Sometimes dye is used before impregnation and other times it is added to the filler and this is called **"B+C" jade**. The only definitive test is infrared (FTIR) spectroscopy. Don't plan on handing bleached jade down to future generations; it will discolor with time and the tiny tunnels create durability problems. Prongs from mountings can dig into the "B" jade, and dishwashing solutions and other substances can damage it over time. Sellers are supposed to disclose treatments, especially when they are not stable, but not all do.

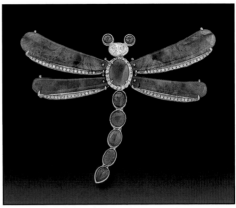

Fig. J.16 California black nephrite. *Pendant, carving, photo: Georg Schmerholz.*

Fig. J.17 Burmese jadeite. *"Imperial dragonfly" and photo courtesy Mason-Kay.*

Fig. J.18 Lavender Burmese jadeite. *Necklace and photo courtesy Mason-Kay.*

Fig. J.19 Blue nephrite from Washington state. *Carving & photo: Deborah Wilson.*

Fig. J.20 Burmese jadeite. *Earrings by Katy Briscoe; photo by Kennon Evett.*

Fig. J.21 Burmese jadeite. *Rings from Jade by Nikolai; photo by Nikolai Tsang.*

When buying jade, deal with reputable jewelers. Ask how and if it has been treated. Have the treatment information written on the receipt, and have expensive pieces checked by gem labs which have the experience and equipment required to test jade.

Jadeite Pricing Versus Nephrite Pricing

A key determinant of the price of jadeite is its treatment status. A bleached and polymer-impregnated jadeite cabochon that looks like a $50,000 untreated cabochon might sell for less than $500, while if it is also dyed, it might sell for less than $50. Another key determinant of price is transparency. An untreated jadeite cabochon with a rich green color like a $50,000 semitransparent jadeite cabochon might also sell for less than $500 if it were semiopaque.

Color is naturally very important. A highly saturated green resembling the color of a fine emerald (imperial green) will attain the highest price, assuming the jadeite has good transparency. Semitransparent colorless jadeite is also in high demand among jadeite connoisseurs and can cost thousands of dollar a cabochon, although it does not attain prices as high as those of semitransparent untreated green jadeite. Grayish colors can be significantly lower in value than those that are more pure and saturated. Bluish lavender jadeite is generally less valued than lavender jadeite that is more pinkish.

The pricing of jadeite jewelry can also be significantly affected by its provenance, e.g., owner(s), geographic source, designer, brand, and jade rough source (if the jade was cut from a famous jade boulder, it can sell at a high premium). However, provenance must be substantiated with documentation such as invoices, photos, lab reports, publications and/or authentic marks on the piece.

The intrinsic value of a stone usually brings higher prices for jadeite than nephrite. Generic top quality green jadeite cabochons can command prices in the tens of thousands of dollars. Top quality green nephrite cabochons of the same size can typically be purchased for less than $500 because their transparency and green colors do not match those of fine quality jadeite. The record high auction prices attained for nephrite pieces are usually the result of the historical significance, antique value and provenance of the pieces, instead of the intrinsic value of the jade itself.

Before the 2008 Beijing Olympics, nephrite was viewed more as a trinket than as a worthy jewelry material. However, that changed when the Olympic medals were inlaid with nephrite and people learned that nephrite was the original Chinese "stone of heaven." Since then, jade prices have risen rapidly and the allure of nephrite jade in China has soared, and it is now being used in expensive designer jewelry.

The value factors for uncarved green nephrite cabochons, bangles and beads are similar to those of green jadeite. The greater the transparency, the greener the jade and the more saturated and even the color, the higher the price. The mode of production is also a big price determinant. Nephrite jewelry that is mass produced in Chinese factories costs significantly less than hand carved nephrite. Carvings that are cut by CNC (computer numerically controlled) milling machines cost much less than original carvings. The most prized nephrite color is white, especially among Chinese buyers. The purer the white, the more valuable the stone. Pure white jade from Hotan (aka Khotan and Hetian) commands high premiums over white jade mined in other areas. Some white Hotan pebbles have sold for more than the equivalent of $30,000 in China.

The way nephrite is priced varies depending on cultural and individual preferences. The Chinese for example, tend to prefer pure colors, textures and clarity, whereas many North American carvers like inclusions and variations in color and texture because it enables them to create one-of-a-kind carvings. The most preferred jade tends to attain the highest prices. For additional information, consult *Jade* by Roger Keverne and *Exotic Gems, Volume 4: How to Identify, Evaluate & Select Jade & Abalone Pearls* by Renée Newman.

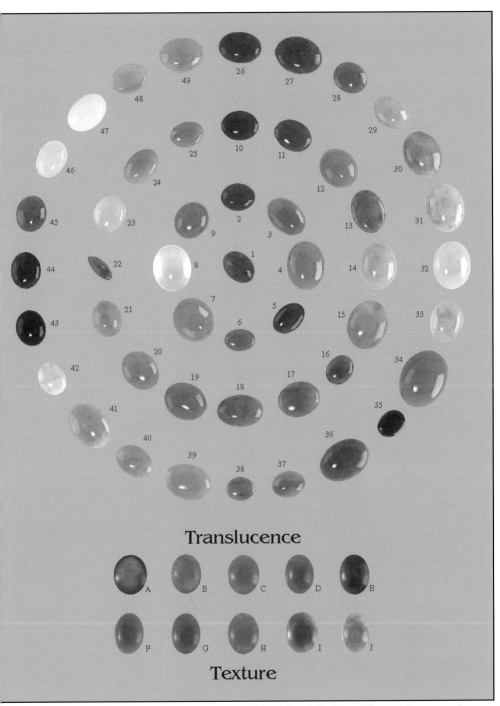

Fig. J.22 Mason-Kay Fine Jade Jewelry "Colors of Jade" chart. The numbers are for identification purposes only. Note: the actual colors of these stones may be slightly different than shown. The printing and developing processes usually alter the true color of gems in photographs. *Chart and stones courtesy Mason-Kay.*

Lapis Lazuli a rock composed primarily of lazurite plus some calcite, pyrite and other minerals, the 9th wedding anniversary stone

For more than 5000 years, lapis lazuli (lapis) has been mined in Northeastern Afghanistan. This is still the world's most important source both in terms of quality and quantity. The name *lapis lazuli* is from the Latin word for stone, *lapis,* and the Persian *lazhward* meaning blue. Up until the Middle Ages, lapis was called *sapphirus,* which also means blue. In ancient texts such as the Bible, the term sapphire most likely refers to lapis lazuli. The Ancient Egyptians, Greeks and Romans not only used lapis for adornment, they ground it up to make eye shadow, medicine and a pigment called ultramarine, which was used in many of the world's famous paintings. Today lapis is one of the most popular stones for men's jewelry and it is used to make beads, watch dials, boxes, figurines and other decorative articles.

The most valued lapis has a natural, even, highly saturated deep violet-blue color that is free of white calcite veining. Dull greenish lapis and lapis that is dyed are the least valued. Dye is used to improve the color and to hide white calcite. Often, the dye is not very stable and may rub off on your skin. A wax coating is commonly used to seal in the dye and to make the polish look better. It's not always possible for salespeople to know if lapis has been dyed. However, if they claim the color is natural and the stone is untreated, have them write this on the receipt. Generally, most lapis beads are dyed. Dye can often be detected by rubbing the stone with cotton dipped in fingernail polish remover or alcohol. Never do this in a conspicuous spot and always get permission first.

The second most important source of lapis after Afghanistan is Chile. However, Chilean lapis tends to contain a lot of white calcite and pyrite, and the color can be relatively light. Consequently it is often dyed. German and Swiss lapis are not lapis lazuli. They are blue dyed jasper, the most widely used lapis imitation.

RI: approx 1.5	**SG**: 2.60–2.90	**Hardness**: 5–6	**Toughness**: Fair to good
Care Tips: Avoid ultrasonics, steamers, high heat & acids. Clean with warm soapy water			

Fig. L.1 Lapis and blue topaz. *Pendant by The Jewelers Bench, Inc; photo by Skip Colflesh.*

Fig. L.2 Afghan lapis peacock carved by Eberhard Bank of Idar-Oberstein, Germany. *Carving & photo courtesy Sarosi by Timeless Gems.*

Malachite $Cu_2CO_3(OH)_2$—a hydrated copper carbonate; a common ore of copper

As early as 3000 BC malachite was recovered from copper mines in Egypt and Israel. Besides being used for jewelry, charms and ornaments, it was ground into powder and worn as eye make-up. The same powdered pigment is used by painters under the name of "Mountain Green."

Malachite is usually banded with differing shades of green in agate-like patterns, which makes it easy to identify. Beautiful yet affordably priced, it's sold by the piece as cabochons, beads, figurines, mosaics, boxes, and other decorative objects. Often the banding is intermixed with other copper minerals such as blue azurite. In this case, the resulting material is called **azurmalachite**.

Malachite has a Mohs hardness of 3.5–4 so it is easily scratched. It's also sensitive to heat, acids and ammonia. Sometimes malachite is impregnated with wax or epoxy to improve the polish, hide small cracks and increase durability.

Currently the Democratic Republic of the Congo is the major producer of malachite Other sources include Arizona, Australia,, Mexico, Namibia, Russia, Tanzania and Zambia.

RI: 1.66–1.91	**SG**: 3.6–4.0	**Hardness**: 3.5–4	**Toughness**: Fair to poor
Care Tips: Avoid ultrasonics, steamers, high heat & acids. Clean with warm soapy water.			

Fig. Ma.1 Malachite. *Carved brooch from Lang Antiques, San Francisco; photo by Cole Bybee.*

Fig. Ma.1 Malachite. *Cufflinks courtesy Lang Antiques, San Francisco; photo by Cole Bybee.*

Fig. Ma.2 Azurmalachite. *Pendant by Patrick Murphy and Emily Chesick; photo by Corey Morse.*

Moonstone & Other Selected Feldspars

(A group of closely related minerals), Moonstone—A birthstone for June

Over half of the earth's crust is composed of minerals from the feldspar group but only some of the varieties are known as gemstones. All varieties require special care since they can be easily cleaved (split) and chipped. In fact, "feldspar" is derived from "field" and "spar," words that refer to any shiny rock that cleaves easily.

Hardness: 6–6.5	Toughness: Poor	Optic Character: DR, biaxial; AGG reaction common
RI: 1.52–1.54 (moonstone & amazonite); 1.54–1.55 (oligoclase); 1.56–1.57 (labradorite)		
SG: 2.54–2.63 (moonstone & amazonite); 2.62–2.69 (oligoclase); 2.67–2.72 (labradorite)		
Cleavage: Perfect (x2); parting: common. Stability to heat: May crack; amazonite may also lose color		
Care tips: Avoid ultrasonics, steamers, heat, acids & rough handling. Warm, soapy water is safe.		
Treatments: Normally none for moonstone & sunstone. Amazonite may be impregnated with wax or polymers; andesine-labradorite is usually diffusion treated; yellow labradorite is often irradiated.		

MOONSTONE: In India, people once believed that moonstone was solidified moonlight. It is supposed to bring good fortune and help to foretell future events. Moonstones are noted for a floating light effect and sheen called **adularescence**. This phenomenon results from alternating layers of two kinds of feldspar (usually orthoclase and albite) which cause light to scatter. High moonstone cabochons may resemble cat's-eye gems due to the concentration of light along the top of the stone. Moonstone can be near transparent to translucent and is typically white, colorless or light grayish blue, but it may also be yellow, orange, brown, blue or green. It retails from about $5/ct up to $300/ct for the most valued stones, which are blue and near transparent. Major sources are India, Myanmar, Sri Lanka and Tanzania.

LABRADORITE: This name most often refers to a dark feldspar, first found in Labrador, that displays a flash of color(s) when viewed at certain angles. This optical effect, called **labradorescence**, is typically bright blue, but it can also be green, yellow or orange. In a more general sense, "labradorite" includes some feldspars that are more transparent. Examples would be Oregon sunstone, Mexican labradorite and **rainbow labradorite**, a nearly transparent, colorless stone with multicolored labradorescence. This labradorite is often sold as **rainbow moonstone** and is found in Madagascar.

Spectrolite is a trade name for a labradorite from Finland with rich color flashes. Andesine labradorite, a pale yellow, red or green feldspar, is commonly diffusion treated to turn it a strong red, green or orange color.

YELLOW ORTHOCLASE: A collector stone, this is usually transparent and faceted.

SUNSTONE: There are two main types of sunstone. The best known, aventurine feldspar (oligoclase), has glittery red or golden inclusions of hematite. Another type, labradorite, is orange, yellow, red, green or near colorless and has copper inclusions. It's the state gem of Oregon, and in sizes of one carat and above retails for about $70–$1500/ct. For more information on sunstone and other feldspars, consult *Exotic Gems: Volume 1* by Renée Newman.

AMAZONITE (Amazon stone, microcline): A green to bluish-green stone, which is sometimes sold as "Pikes Peak jade" in Colorado. It's also found in Africa, Brazil, India, Russia and Southeast Asia. It's usually translucent but can be transparent.

Fig. F.1 Sunstone, state gem of Oregon. *Cut by John Dyer; photo by Priscilla Dyer.*

Fig. F.2 Rare transparent amazonite from Luc Yen, Vietnam. *Pala International; photo: Mia Dixon.*

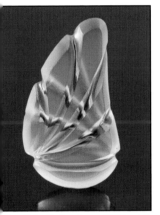

Fig. F.3 Orthoclase (8.74 cts). *Carved by Sherris Cottier Shank; photo by A. Bathrop Akanni.*

Fig. F.4 Carved labradorite. *Ring by Zaffiro; photo by Elizabeth Gualtieri.*

Fig. F.5 Rainbow moonstone. (labradorite). *Gem: Boston Gems; photo: Robert & Orasa Weldon.*

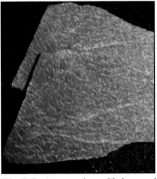

Fig. F.6 Moonstone. *Ring © Eve J. Alfillé; photo: Matthew Arden.*

Fig.F.7 Amazonite. *Slabs and photo from Mark Anderson of Different Seasons Jewelry.*

Fig.F.8 Sunstone from Tanzania. (oligoclase). *Gem & photo from New Era Gems.*

Opal SiO$_2$nH$_2$O—Silica + water, about 3–10% water in opals with a play-of-color
An October birthstone and 14th wedding anniversary stone

Historically, opals were said to bring good fortune because they possessed the colors and powers of all gemstones. The ancient Latin name for opal was *Opalus*, which was apparently derived from the Sanskrit *Upala* meaning "precious stone." The Greek word for opal, *opállios*, means "to see a change (of color)."

White opal was probably first mined at Czerwenitza, Czechoslovakia (formerly Hungary). Archival evidence shows that this mine was in operation in the 14th century, but it most likely was worked much earlier. In Mexico, fire opal was probably known to the Aztecs as early as the 13th century. They believed that fire opal represented all the virtues of the sun—energy, light, warmth and life itself.

In the late 1800's Australia became the most important source of fine opal when white opal and boulder opal were discovered there. In 1902, black opal was discovered in New South Wales at Lightning Ridge. Then in 1915 a new mining area opened in Cooper Pedy and became Australia's largest opal producer.

Originally, opals were mined with picks shovels and explosives; the loose dirt was removed from the pits by hand in buckets. By the 1970's more mechanized tools were used for opal mining. Consequently, it was possible to extract more opal than ever before. Up through the 1990's, major amounts of opal became available and prices decreased. However, since 2000, the supply of opal in Australia and the population of the mining towns have dropped significantly. As a result, high quality opal has become scare and opal prices have been rising.

In 1996 white opal was discovered in Ethiopia and more deposits have been found there since then. Other sources of opal include Mexico, Brazil, the U.S. and Honduras.

If you were to examine opal under an electron microscope at 20,000X magnification, you would see a mass of closely packed, tiny silica spheres. Opal shows a **play-of-color** (a shifting of spectral colors) when the spheres are of uniform size and arranged in regular layers. This type of opal is called **precious opal**. The color or range of colors of precious opal are determined by the size of the spheres. Light bends and splits as it passes through the spheres, causing spectral colors to appear at different angles. The brighter and more distinctive the play-of-color, the better the opal. Not all opals show a play-of-color. However, they do share the following properties:

RI: 1.44–1.47, Mexican opal: as low as 1.37, but usually 1.42–1.43		SG: 1.98–2.20
Hardness: 5.5–6.5	**Cleavage**: None	**Optic Character**: SR, ADR common
Pleochroism: None	**Light Stability**: Stable	**Crystal System**: Mainly amorphous

Reaction to Heat: Sudden temperature changes may cause opals to crack or craze. Over heating can ca crazing and turn opals white or brownish causing the play-of-color to disappear.

Toughness: Very poor to fair depending on source and type of opal. Reputable dealers usually keep their opals for a period of time to verify they are not susceptible to crazing, a network of fine cracks.

Care Tips: Avoid ultrasonics, steamers, heat & chemicals. Don't immerse assembled opals in water

Treatments: Sometimes impregnated with oil, wax, resin, or plastic to improve play-of-color, disgui cracks, and/or increase durability; sometimes dyed, smoked or sugar treated to simulate black opal

Fig. Op.1 Mexican freeform fire opal. *Earrings by Hubert; photo by Diamond Graphics.*

Fig. Op.2 Lightning Ridge black opal. *Bear Essentials; photo: Tino Hammid.*

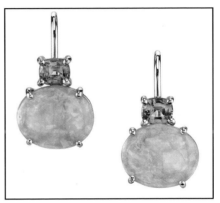

Fig. Op.3 Australian opal accented with spinels. *Ring design by Rémy Rotinier; ring and photo from Omi Privé..*

Fig. Op.4 Ethiopian opals accented with tsavorites. *Earrings by Sarosi of Timeless Gems; photo by Diamond Graphics.*

Fig. Op. 5 & 6 Scanning electron micrographs of opals at 40,000x magnification. Left: precious opal, right: potch. *Photos from Division of Minerals and Energy Resources, Primary Industries and Resources, South Australia.*

Fig. Op.7 Mexican fire opal with very bright play-of-color. *Opal from Emil Weis Opals; photo by Tanja Schutz.*

Opal Varieties, Types and Trade Names

COMMON OPAL and **POTCH**: Opal with **no** play-of-color and translucent to near opaque. It occurs in various body colors; blue opal is the most expensive and can retail for as much as $350/ct. Green and pink opal are also popular varieties.

LIGHT OPAL (includes white opal, grey opal, crystal and jelly opal): Opal with a play-of-color and a light body color. WHITE OPAL is the most common type. It typically has an off-white body color and is translucent. White opals with a brilliant play-of-color can retail for several hundred dollars per carat. When a light opal is transparent to semitransparent and has a distinct play-of-color, it is called a CRYSTAL OPAL or SEMICRYSTAL OPAL. Crystal opal is the most valued light opal. In its highest qualities, it can cost more than $4000/ct retail. A WATER OPAL is near transparent, near colorless, and shows a play-of-color or none at all. HYDROPHANE OPAL is opal that readily absorbs water. Ethiopia and Andamooka, Australia are the best-known sources of hydrophane opal. According to Bear Williams of Stone Group Labs, a turbid look can develop over time when oils are absorbed in hydrophane opal, but dirty water speeds the effect.

BLACK OPAL: "Black opal" is often used as a generic term for any opal that has a play-of-color against a dark background. However, CIBJO, the World Jewellery Confederation, now defines it as a black to very dark opal. The darker and blacker the background, the higher the price. Opals that were formerly called semi-black are now called dark opals by the Australian Gemstone Industry Council (AGIC). Top-grade black opal can wholesale for $20,000/ct. Some exceptional stones have even sold for more. If the stone is transparent to semitransparent and very dark with a play-of-color, the stone is classified as a BLACK CRYSTAL OPAL.

BOULDER OPAL: A layer of opal that is naturally attached to the rock (usually ironstone) in which it is found. This opal is found in boulders whose cracks and spaces have been infiltrated with opal. Boulder opal, which can resemble either light or dark opal, is typically cut in irregular shapes. Gem quality boulder opal may sell for $5000 to $60,000 dollars per piece, but you can get attractive stones for a few hundred dollars. Since it is not solid opal, it costs less than black opal. Boulder opal is mined in Queensland, Australia.

MATRIX OPAL or **OPAL-IN-MATRIX**: Stones with veins, grains or patches of opal scattered randomly throughout the **matrix** (host rock—the rock in which a mineral, fossil or pebble is found, usually ironstone). Boulder matrix opal is found in Queensland. If it's from the Yowah or Koroit mining areas of South Queensland, it's often called "Yowah opal" or "Koroit opal" respectively. The patches and lines of opal in their matrix may form distinctive patterns, which sometimes adds to its value. Matrix opal normally sells for much less than boulder opal. Its price is determined by the amount, type, and quality of the opal within the matrix. NUTS are small rounded matrix masses with a solid opal kernel in the center or a network of thin opal veins.

Another more porous matrix opal is found in Andamooka and is often dyed black to simulate black opal. Mexico also has a distinctive variety of matrix opal.

FIRE OPAL: A transparent to translucent opal with a red, orange, yellow or brownish body color with or without a play-of-color. Mexico is the main source, but it is also found in Ethiopia, Tanzania, Brazil and Oregon.

The most valued fire opal is red or reddish orange, transparent, and has a bright intense play-of-color with multiple hues. This quality can retail for more than $3000/ct. Commercial qualities sell for less than $100/ct. Low quality fire opals with poor transparency and dull colors can sell for less than $20/ct.

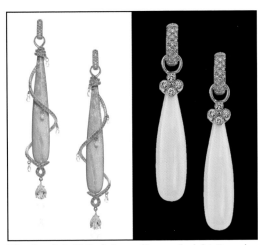

Fig. Op.8 Opal without play-of-color. *Opals: Gerald Stockton; photo © Newman.*

Fig. Op. 9 & 10 Left Australian opal, right: Peruvian pink opal. *Earrings and photo: Erica Courtney.*

Fig. Op.12 Left to right; a crystal shell opal, a Lightning Ridge crystal opal and a semicrystal opal. *Opals: Gerald Stockton; photo © Renée Newman.*

Fig. Op.11 Ethiopian opal. *Cufflinks and photo by Ashleigh Branstetter.*

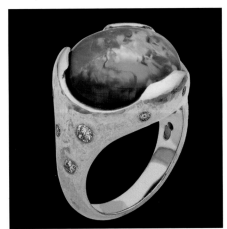

Fig. Op. 13 Lightning Ridge black opal. *Ring & photo by Hopkins Opal.*

Op. 14 Lightning Ridge black opal. *"World of Opals" Los Angeles 11/24/2014 Bonhams Auction; photo © Bonhams, all rights reserved.*

For more information on evaluating fire opal and common opal, consult Renée Newman's *Exotic Gems: Volume 2*, which devotes two chapters to these opals. *Exotic Gems: Volume 3* provides an in-depth discussion of matrix opal.

Treatments, Assembled Stones, Etc.

Opal is occasionally impregnated with oil, resin, or plastic to improve the play-of-color and to prevent or disguise crazing. There are also various techniques for simulating black opal. These include smoke impregnation, backing with black or colored paint, and treatment with dye, silver nitrate or sugar carbonized by acid. One should avoid repolishing or applying solvents to treated opal.

If you'd like a stone with a black-opal look at an inexpensive price, consider getting an opal doublet or triplet. An OPAL DOUBLET (also called DOUBLET OPAL) is a thin slice of opal usually cemented with black glue to another material such as potch opal, chalcedony or glass. It often sells for about 1/10 the amount that it would cost if it were a solid, non-assembled opal. If a doublet also has a protective top of colorless quartz or glass, then it is called an OPAL TRIPLET or a TRIPLET OPAL. Triplets are usually less expensive than doublets because less opal is used. Do not confuse these assembled stones with boulder opal, which has a naturally attached backing. Often you can detect man-made stones by looking at them from the side. A doublet typically has a straight separation line whereas a boulder opal has an uneven one. There are also fake opal stones. One is called SLOCUM STONE and another OPALITE. Hong Kong is a major producer of imitation opal. Synthetic opal is grown in Japan and Russia.

Factors Which Affect Opal Value

OPAL TYPE: Solid black opal costs more than similar looking boulder opal. Matrix opals and assembled stones are the least expensive types. The price difference between a natural opal and an assembled opal of similar appearance is huge so ask sellers to identify the opal both verbally and on the receipt.

BRIGHTNESS: The more brilliant and intense the flashes of color and the higher the play-of-color to background ratio the better the stone. Brightness is one of the most important value factors and may be measured on a scale of 1 to 5 with 5 being the brightest. Level 5 stones often seem brighter in subdued light than they do in sunlight or a spotlight. Level 1 stones show faint color only under sunlight and those that are level 2 have a dull play of color under sunlight or spotlight. View the opal in different orientations and examine brightness both under a direct light source and away from it. Opals that maintain their brightness away from the light and in multiple directions are the most highly valued.

BODY TONE (The darkness or lightness of the background color): Body tone is graded by the Australian Gemstone Industry Council (AGIC) on a scale of N1 to N9, with N1 being the darkest (N stands for neutral). Stones with tonal grades of N1–N4 are classified as black opals. Those with tones N5–N6 are called dark opals. Light opals have a tonal range from N7–N9. A black body color is more valued than a gray or light body tone, all other factors being equal. When determining body tone, look at the top of the stone. Black opals with an N1 body tone are very rare. The body tone rating is normally not applicable to near colorless, transparent crystal opals.

PLAY-OF-COLOR: The dominant color(s) and the combination of colors are both important. Intense red is the most rare and thus the most prized. In terms of value, it's followed by orange, yellow, green and blue, the most plentiful color. The rarest and most valuable opals display a bright full spectrum play-of-color from all angles.

Fig. Op. 15 Boulder opals. *Earrings by Paula Crevoshay; photo by Crevoshay Studio.*

Fig. Op. 16 Koroit matrix opal. *Pendant by Whitney Robinson; photo: Hanna Cook-Wallace.*

Fig. Op.17 Mexican fire opal. *Gems and photo from Columbia Gem House.*

Fig. Op.18 Serbian green opal. *Ring by Paula Crevoshay; Crevoshay Studio.*

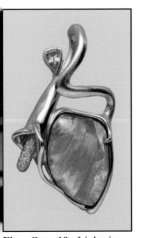

Fig. Op. 19 Lightning Ridge opal. *Pin & photo: Hanna Cook-Wallace.*

Fig.Op. 20 Opal (16.81 cts) and Ethiopian opal beads. *Necklace and photo: Paula Crevoshay.*

Op. 21 Smoked Ethiopian Welo opal. *Stone Group Laboratories; photo by Dean Brennan.*

COLOR PATTERN: The diffracted colors in opals are displayed in various patterns such as: PINFIRE—small pinpoint-like color specks; BROAD FLASH—sheets of color normally covering a large section or all of a stone's surface; CHECKERBOARD—square patches of color set close together (a very rare pattern); FANCY PATTERNS—unusual patterns that resemble things such as Chinese writing, ribbons, straw, floral, cat's-eye stones, etc. Pinfire and small type patterns are generally less valued than broad patterns or large flashes. Distinct patterns like checkerboards and ribbons are especially valuable. The term "harlequin" is often applied to opal patterns with square or angular patches of color set close together like a mosaic. True harlequin patterns, however, have brightly colored diamond shapes and are almost nonexistent in opal.

TRANSPARENCY: For light opal and fire opal, the higher the transparency, the more valuable the stone. For black opal, the nearly opaque, blacker stones tend to be more highly valued than those with greater transparency.

SHAPE: The most sought-after traditional shape is a well-formed oval. It tends to bring a higher price than other shapes because it's in greater demand, it's easier to set, and valuable opal material is sacrificed when stones are cut as ovals. Many jewelers and designers, however, prefer other shapes, especially freeforms because they are more distinctive. Unusual freeforms may sell for more than ovals, especially after they are mounted.

CUT & THICKNESS OF THE COLOR BAR: All else being equal, domed cabochons tend to be more valued than flat ones because they usually have a thicker layer of play-of-color opal above the girdle. Excessive weight on the bottom and a thin or unsymmetrical profile can all reduce the value of an opal.

SIZE & CARAT WEIGHT: Stones under a carat are generally worth less per carat than larger ones. If a stone is unusually large, it may be worth less per carat than stones more suitable for general jewelry use. Boulder opals are typically priced by size rather than carat weight. The larger the opal the higher the price.

IMPERFECTIONS: Opal value decreases when there are eye-visible inclusions in the stone such as sand or gypsum. The larger and more noticeable they are, the greater their impact on value. Cracks drastically reduce value. A common opal flaw is **crazing**—a thin, network of fractures that resembles a spider web. When deep, it has a serious impact on price. Opals with a high water content are most subject to crazing. There are ways of concealing crazing, but no honest opal dealer would do that without disclosing it. Many dealers offer some type of guarantee against crazing that is typically valid for one year. However, this guarantee does not cover cracks, which are usually the result of abuse or poor setting skills. To prevent crazing in dry environments such as safe deposit boxes, some dealers store their opals in distilled water. Others say this is unnecessary. At any rate, water does not hurt the opal. Opals sometimes have pattern lines which look like cracks but aren't. These lines are natural changes in the pattern of an opal and are not regarded as flaws.

Since opals are relatively soft and fragile, they require special care. Avoid heat and sudden changes of temperature. Do not wear them while sunbathing or set them on a sunny window sill or under hot lights. Do not clean them in ultrasonics. Instead, wash them in lukewarm water with a mild soap and soft cloth. (Opal doublets and triplets, however, should not be immersed in water.) Store opal jewelry separately in cloth pouches. Take rings off when doing housework and engaging in sports. With proper care, opals can give you a lifetime of enjoyment.

Two good sources for more information on opal evaluation are *Australian Precious Opal* by Andrew Cody and *Opal Identification and Value* by Paul Downing.

Figs. Op. 22–24 Lightning Ridge black opals with three different brightness levels ranging from about 4.5 on the left to 3.5 in the center and 2.5 on the right (the brightness can look different in a photo than in person and varies depending on the angle from which the opal is viewed). *Jewelry and photos courtesy Cary Harris.*

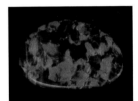

Fig. Op.25 Milky opal with low brightness.

Fig. Op.26 Side view of an opal doublet. *Photo © Renée Newman.*

Fig. Op.27 Face-up view of doublet in Fig. Op.26.

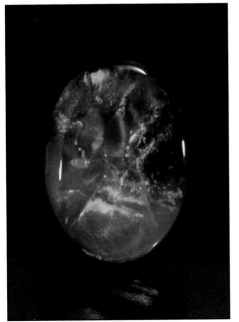

Fig. Op. 28 Lightning Ridge black opal (7.46 cts) with a ribbon pattern and rolling flash. *Opal from Bear Essentials; photo by Robert Weldon.*

Op. 29 Lightning Ridge black opal (28.25 cts) with a rolling broad flash pattern. *"World of Opals" Los Angeles 11/24/2014 Bonhams Auction; photo © Bonhams, all rights reserved.*

Peridot (Olivine group, forsterite species) $(Mg,Fe)_2SiO_4$—Magnesium iron silicate, August birthstone, 16th wedding anniversary stone

According to legend, wearing peridot will protect you from evil spirits. This rich, yellowish-green gem, also called chrysolite, olivine or forsterite, has sometimes been mistaken for emerald. Many of Cleopatra's "emeralds" were probably peridot. Adding further confusion, peridot was called topaz in ancient times.

Peridot is attractive, yet affordable. You can purchase a high quality peridot for less than $600/ct retail. The greener the stone and the better the clarity, the higher the value rises. Large stones are available and it is widely used in tumbled form as beads for necklaces. If yellow or orange colors complement your skin, then peridot jewelry should look good on you. It is particularly flattering to people with blond or red hair.

Peridot has been mined for more than 3500 years. The oldest source is St. John's Island, Egypt, in the Red Sea. Pakistan and Arizona are the main sources today. Other deposits include Myanmar, China, Afghanistan, Brazil, Kenya and Norway. Physical and optical characteristics of peridot are given below:

RI: 1.64–1.69	SG: 3.27– 3.45	Hardness: 6.5–7		Toughness: Fair to good
Pleochroism: weak		Crystal Sys: Orthorhombic		Optic Char: DR, biaxial + or -
Stability to Heat: Rapid or uneven heat changes can cause peridot to crack or break.				
Reaction to Chemicals: Attacked by sulfuric and HCl acid. Acidic perspiration of some people over a long period may etch the surface. Jewelers should never put peridot in pickling solutions.				
Care Tips: Ultrasonics are risky; avoid steamers, acids and abrupt temperature changes.				
Treatments: Normally not treated; the color is natural. May be fracture-filled if fractures are present.				

Fig. P.1 Pakistan peridot (217 ct). *"Green Dream" carving by Larry Woods of Jewels From The Woods; photo by John Parrish.*

Fig. P.2 Peridot. *Necklace by Catherine Lehman; photo courtesy Stephen Vincent Design.*

Right: Fig. P.3 Peridot. *Ring & photo courtesy Omi Privé.*

Spodumene LiAlSi$_2$O$_6$—Lithium and aluminum silicate

KUNZITE, the best-known spodumene variety, is pink to purple. Found in California in 1902, it was named after George Frederick Kunz, a famous gemologist and former vice-president of Tiffany & Co. Much of the kunzite available today comes from Afghanistan and Brazil and is irradiated and/or heated to intensify its color. The color can fade over time with prolonged exposure to light or heat. Kunzite is typically eye-clean and low priced. Well-cut stones of high clarity usually retail for under $300/ct.

Spodumene can also be colorless to yellow (called TRIPHANE)or green in color and is generally referred to as spodumene with or without the color identifier. Like kunzite, it's usually found as large crystals, it is often irradiated, and it frequently originates from Brazil or Afghanistan, though also found in Madagascar, Nigeria, Pakistan and the USA. Yellowish green to yellow spodumene tends to have a very light to medium-light tone and generally retails for less than $200/ct.

The rare natural-color emerald-green variety of spodumene colored by chromium is called HIDDENITE. It was discovered in the area of Hiddenite, North Carolina in 1879 by William Hidden. The deposit is very small and production has always been sporadic. Top-color hiddenites from North Carolina cost about $3500-$4500/ct.

RI: 1.66–1.68	SG: 3.14–3.21	Hardness: 6.5–7	Monoclinic	Toughness: Fair to poor
Trichroism: Moderate to strong		Cleavage: Perfect in two directions	DR, biaxial positive	
Care Tips: Avoid ultrasonic cleaners, rough handling, acids and prolonged light and heat.				

Fig. Sp.1 Kunzite. *Bracelet by Hubert, Inc; photo by Diamond Graphics.*

Sp.2 Hiddenite from Stony Point, Alexander County, North Carolina (5 x 1.3 x 0.5.cm). *Bill Larson Collection; photo: Jeff Scovil.*

Fig. Sp.3 Kunzite from Afghanistan (104 cts). *Necklace and photo by Loretta Castoro.*

Ruby & Sapphire (Corundum) Al_2O_3—Aluminum Oxide

Ruby—July birthstone; sapphire—September birthstone;
Ruby—15th & 40th anniversary stone; sapphire—5th & 45th anniversary stone

Ruby and sapphire have a lot in common. They are the same mineral—corundum. They have the same physical characteristics. Both have been considered regal and sacred. In ancient India the ruby was called the king of gems and the Hindus thought that if they offered a ruby to the god Krishna, they would be reborn as an emperor. In England the ruby was used for coronation rings. Sapphires were worn by kings and queens for good luck and they were set in rings for bishops and cardinals. Their blue color symbolized heaven.

Color is what distinguishes ruby from sapphire. Rubies are red and sapphires are either blue or another color such as green, orange, pink, yellow, purple, colorless or black (sapphire colors other than blue are called **fancy colors**). It wasn't until about 1800 that ruby and sapphire were recognized as being the same mineral. Before then, red spinel and garnet were also called ruby. The name was derived from the Latin word for red, *rubeus*. "Sapphire" is probably from the Greek word *sappheiros* meaning blue.

Rubies and sapphires are harder than all other gems except diamonds. Their superior hardness combined with the lack of cleavage makes them a very durable gem. It also makes them valuable for industrial purposes. They've been produced synthetically for use as laser windows, tips in ballpoint pins, and jewel bearings in watches, meters and aircraft instruments. The properties of ruby and sapphire are:

RI: 1.76–1.78	**SG**: 3.95–4.05	**Hardness**: 9	**Crystal System**: Trigonal
Cleavage: None, stones may show parting			**Optic Character**: DR, uniaxial negative

Toughness: Excellent, except for lead glass-filled & fractured stones; may abrade easily if improperly hea

Pleochroism: Ruby—strong purplish red and orangy red; sapphire—moderate to strong violetish blue and greenish blue; fancy-color sapphires—weak to strong dichroism

Stability to Light: Stable except for irradiated yellow and orange sapphires, which may fade

Care Tips: Ultrasonics and steamers are safe if stones are not oiled or cavity or fracture-filled. Lead glass-filled rubies can be easily damaged with household cleaners, acids and jeweler's torches.

Treatments: Assume that corundum is heated unless otherwise stated. Unheated stones are available. Fracture filling with oil, epoxy or glass—common in ruby; diffusion treatment or dyeing—sometimes done; Irradiation—rare, produces yellow or orange sapphire from colorless or light yellow varieties.

Varieties

RUBY: In 1896 German mineralogist Max Bauer wrote: *A clear transparent, and faultless ruby of a uniform deep red colour is at the present time the most valuable stone known.* Today diamonds have surpassed rubies in value, but Bauer's description of a top-quality ruby is still valid. In addition, a strong red fluorescence is desirable and top-grade stones have a minimal amount of black, gray or brown. Most of the stones that have met these color criteria are from the Mogok area of Myanmar (Burma) and are sold at premium prices. Do not assume, though, that a ruby is good quality if it originates from Mogok. Likewise, don't assume that rubies from other localities such as Cambodia, Kenya, Madagascar, Mozambique, Sri Lanka, Tanzania, Thailand, and Vietnam must be inferior. High-quality rubies have originated from all of these sources.

Fig. RS.1 Kashmir sapphire (27.07 carats). *Gem: Bear Essentials; photo by Bear Williams.*

Fig. RS.2 Rubies (5.50 cts tw). *Earrings and photo courtesy Jye Luxury Collection.*

Fig. RS.3 Orange sapphire from Sri Lanka (5.60 cts, unheated). *Ring by Cynthia Renée Inc; photo by Robert & Orasa Weldon.*

Fig. RS.4 Padparadscha from Sri Lanka (2.22 cts, unheated). *Gem from Mayer & Watt; photo by Geoffrey Watt.*

Fig. RS.5 Purple and yellow sapphires. *Ring © Eve J. Alfillé; photo by Matthew Arden.*

Fig. RS.6 Australian parti-colored sapphire (4.84 cts, untreated). *Cut by John Dyer; photo by Priscilla Dyer.*

On May 12, 2015, a 25.59-carat Cartier Burmese ruby ring sold for US$32.42 million at a Geneva Sotheby's auction. This was the highest total price and per-carat price (US$1,266,901/ct) ever paid for a ruby as of this writing. This doesn't mean that all stones sold as rubies are worth a lot of money. Some nearly opaque rubies and lead-glass filled "rubies" sell for $10/ct. Lead glass-filled "rubies" are also called **composite rubies** or **hybrid rubies.** Many trade members are opposed to them being called "rubies" because they lack the durability of ruby and contain a high percentage of glass.

SAPPHIRE: When used by itself, the term **sapphire** normally refers to the blue variety. In its highest qualities, it is more expensive than the other varieties. As of this writing the highest per-carat price paid for a sapphire is $243,703/ct. It was for a 27.68-carat Kashmir sapphire at a Hong Kong Sotheby's auction on Oct. 7, 2015. Kashmir sapphires are rare because mining in Kashmir has been extremely limited for decades.

Opinions differ as to what is the best sapphire hue. Some say pure blue, others say violetish blue. Most dealers agree, however, that greenish blues are less valuable. Dealers also have different tone preferences. Some prefer medium tones of blue while others prefer medium-dark tones. Pale, blackish or grayish stones, however, cost the least. Kashmir sapphires have the highest prestige, followed by those from Burma and then Sri Lanka. Today, Madagascar is the major producer of sapphire. Thailand, Cambodia and Australia have also been important sources. Sapphire is also found in India, Montana, China and various African countries. Sapphires are usually heat treated. Their outer surface is sometimes darkened by diffusion treatment, but this must always be disclosed. Sapphires impregnated with cobalt colored lead glass sell for the lowest prices because of durability problems and their high glass content. Like nearly opaque sapphires, they sometimes sell for as little as $10/ct.

PADPARADSCHA: A pinkish-orange sapphire, padparadscha is the rarest and most prized of all the fancy sapphires. Its name is believed to have come from the Sinhalese word for the lotus flower, which has a similar color. Frequently, orange sapphire is called padparadscha, but most dealers agree that both pink and orange hues must be present for a stone to be a true padparadscha; many say the color must be natural. As of this writing, the auction price record for a padparadscha is $52,966/ct. set on Nov, 29, 2011 at a Christie's Hong Kong auction for a 14.65 ct Sri Lankan padparadscha.

PINK SAPPHIRE: Next to the padparadscha, this is the most highly prized of all the fancy sapphires. Since "pink" is a synonym of "light red," and since fine rubies cost more than sapphires, many Asian dealers prefer to call pink sapphires rubies. The jewelry trade in western countries prefers to treat the pink sapphire as a unique stone with its own merits, rather than as a second-rate ruby. High quality pink sapphires can cost several thousand dollars per carat.

ORANGE, PURPLE, YELLOW OR GREEN SAPPHIRE: Madagascar, East Africa, Sri Lanka, Thailand and Montana are the main sources of these sapphires. A high percentage of green sapphire is found in Australia. Of these four sapphire colors, natural color orange has been the most valued, but now purple is almost as valuable as orange. Green is typically the lowest priced; and yellow is usually the most readily available.

COLORLESS SAPPHIRE (WHITE SAPPHIRE): This sapphire is made by heat-treating light-colored sapphire. White sapphire is a popular diamond substitute.

STAR SAPPHIRE AND STAR RUBY: Star corundum with a fine blue or red color is rare. Gray, maroon and black star stones are easier to find, and their prices can be relatively low.

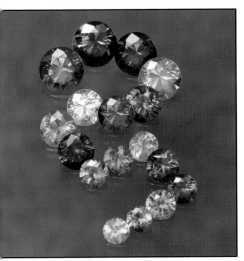

Fig. RS.8 Golden sapphire. *Ring from Hubert, Inc; photo by Diamond Graphics.*

Fig. RS.7 Color range of Rock Creek Montana sapphires. *Gems from Sapphires of Montana; photo by Sherman Pike.*

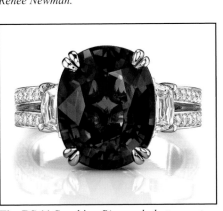

Fig. RS.9 Lead glass-filled "ruby" under 10-power magnification showing typical gas bubbles. *Photo © Renée Newman.*

Fig. RS.10 Star sapphire (14 carats). *Art Deco platinum ring from Lang Antiques, San Francisco; photo by Cole Bybee.*

Fig. RS.11 Sapphire. *Ring and photo courtesy Omi Privé.*

Fig. RS.12 Untreated fancy-color Tanzanian sapphire. *Cut by John Dyer & Co; photo by Priscilla Dyer.*

Spinel MgAl$_2$O$_4$—Magnesium aluminum oxide
22nd wedding anniversary stone

If you're looking for a natural gem that resembles a ruby but costs less, consider getting a spinel. It's durable, comparatively hard and typically has a better clarity and brilliance than a ruby. Not all red spinels can pass as rubies, but many do. Some of the world's largest and most famous "rubies" are really spinels, such as the "Black Princes Ruby" and the 361-ct "Timur Ruby" in the English crown jewels. Spinel comes in other colors such as blue, pink, lavender, orange and black, but red is the most valued.

Natural spinel does not enjoy the popularity that it merits. One reason for this is that it's often confused with the synthetic spinel used in inexpensive birthstone rings and costume jewelry. In addition, natural spinel is not available in large quantities, so it's not widely known and advertised. However, custom jewelers and collectors who like unusual gems appreciate spinel.

The main sources of spinel are Myanmar (Burma) and Sri Lanka. Other localities include Thailand, Cambodia, Tanzania, Russia, Tajikistan and Vietnam. Spinel is often a by-product of the search for ruby and sapphire. Its properties are as follows:

RI: 1.71–1.72 (gem spinel)	**SG**: 3.57 - 3.63 (black spinel, up to 4.0)		**Crystal Sys**: Cubic
Cleavage: Poorly developed	**Hardness**: 8	**Toughness**: Good	**Optic Character**: SR
Stability to Light: Stable. Under intense heat, light-colored stones may fade.			**Pleochroism**: None
Care Tips: Ultrasonics and steamers are usually safe.	**Reaction to Chemicals**: none		
Treatments: Usually none, but occasionally oiled or heated to improve color, clarity and transparency. In May 2015, the GRS lab announced appearance of heat and cobalt diffusion treated blue spinel.			

Varieties

RED SPINEL: The most valuable red spinel resembles high-quality ruby. On September 24, 2015 a nineteenth-century 50.13-carat red spinel brooch/pendant was sold for $1,362,702 at a Bonhams New Bond Street auction in London. Named the "Hope Spinel," it was from Tajikistan and set the auction per-carat price record for spinel of $29,217/ct. As of this writing, the highest total auction price paid for spinel jewelry is $5,214,348 at a May 18, 2011 Christie's Geneva auction. It was for an Imperial Mughal necklace with eleven red spinels weighing 1,131.59 carats. Myanmar is the primary source for red spinel.

PINK SPINEL: This resembles pink sapphire but costs about 20–30% less.

ORANGE SPINEL: Its color range is from yellow-orange to red-orange.

BLUE SPINEL: Fine blue colors are hard to find. This spinel tends to be grayish or very dark. Intense blue stones naturally colored by cobalt are especially rare and sought after by collectors. These are generally from Sri Lanka or Vietnam.

LAVENDER & VIOLET SPINEL: It often has light tones, but can also be purple.

BLACK SPINEL: This spinel is a good option for people who want a black gemstone of natural color. It's mined in Thailand and is the lowest priced spinel. Due to high iron content, it's magnetic.

STAR SPINEL: This is very rare and may be red, violet, blue, purple, gray or black with 4 or 6 rays.

Fig. S.1 Rough and cut spinel from Tunduru and Morogoro, Tanzania. Tanzania is noted for producing a variety of colors of spinel and other gems such as sapphire and zircon. *Gemstones cut by Larry Woods of Jewels from the Woods and Shawn Maddox; photo by John Parrish.*

Fig. S.2 North Vietnamese spinel (2.80 ct) cut by Richard Homer. *Ring by Thomas Dailing; photo by Azad.*

Fig. S.3 North Vietnamese spinel (3.30 ct) cut by Richard Homer. *Ring by Thomas Dailing; photo by Azad.*

Fig. S.4 Burmese star spinel (2.05 cts). *Gem from Pala International; photo by Mia Dixon.*

Fig.S.5 Red spinel. *Ring and photo courtesy Omi Privé.*

Tanzanite & Other Zoisites $Ca_3Al_3(SiO_4)_3(OH)$—Calcium aluminum hydroxysilicate, Tanzanite—a December birthstone & 24th wedding anniversary stone

No history, lore or poetry was needed for tanzanite to become one of the most popular gems on the market. You just look at it and fall in love with it. From one angle it may display a rich blue color, from another it can look purple. Along with the blue and purple, there may be flashes of red, green, yellow, orange or brown. What's more, tanzanite can appear one color indoors and another outdoors. A high clarity and transparency add to its beauty.

Tanzanite was discovered in the 1960's in the foothills of Africa's Mt. Kilimanjaro. Later, Henry Platt, vice-president and director of Tiffany's, named the stone after its country of origin, Tanzania. Gem labs and museums generally believe that the term "tanzanite" should be restricted to transparent zoisites that range in color from blue to violet to purple in color. Other colors such as green, yellow and pink are to be called by their mineralogical name ZOISITE. But since "tanzanite" sounds more exotic and appealing, many dealers tend to use it for all transparent zoisites. However, as with sapphire, the unmodified "tanzanite" refers to the blue or violet variety, whereas other colors must be specified, e.g., yellow tanzanite. This practice allows dealers to distinguish between the transparent and nontransparent green varieties. In the marketplace, for example, green tanzanite is transparent green zoisite whereas green zoisite is typically the nontransparent variety used for carvings. Some European mineralogists call the green, nontransparent material, ANYOLITE. Listed below are properties of zoisite.

RI: 1.69–1.70	SG: 3.20–3.40	Hardness: 6–7	Crystal System: Orthorhombic
Cleavage: Perfect in one direction		Optic Character: DR, biaxial positive	
Toughness: Fair to poor; tanzanite's perfect cleavage makes it vulnerable to bumps and knocks.			
Pleochroism: Very strong; in tanzanite, trichroism is blue, purple, and red, green, yellow or brown.			
Reaction to Chemicals: Attacked by hydrochloric and hydrofluoric acid			
Care Tips: Avoid ultrasonics, steamers, abrupt temperature changes and rough handling.			
Treatments: Almost all tanzanite is heated to improve color. On rare occasions, it has been coated.			

TANZANITE: Some dealers prefer a deep blue with a faint purple secondary color whereas others like an equal mix of blue and purple. Most dealers agree, though, that blue stones are worth more than purple ones. Light lavender stones are priced the lowest. You can find large, high-quality, deep-blue tanzanites with purple overtones for less than $1300/ct retail. Attractive light lavender tanzanite is available for less than $500/ct. Prices vary depending on size, quality and availability. Most tanzanite is heat-treated to intensify the color and/or eliminate brown, gray or green. The color is stable.

THULITE: This translucent pink zoisite, often mottled with gray, is used for cabochons or carvings. Also called ROSALINE, thulite is found in Norway, Austria, Greenland, Italy, Australia and the United States.

GREEN, YELLOW, ORANGE or PINK TRANSPARENT ZOISITE: Strong pink transparent zoisite is the most expensive, even more than blue of the same size and quality. Yellow stones are the most rare but tend to be the lowest priced color.

GREEN ZOISITE: Often found with ruby, this translucent to nearly opaque zoisite is often carved. For more information, consult *Exotic Gems, Vol. 1* by Renée. Newman.

Fig. Tz.1 Heat treated tanzanite (74.58 cts). *Cut by J. L White Fine Gemstones; photo by Jeff White.*

Fig. Tz.2 Same tanzanite before heat treatment. *Cut and photographed by Jeff White.*

Fig.Tz.3 Rough of previous tanzanite before cutting (almost 200 cts). *Photo by Jeff White.*

Fig. Tz.4 Unheated tanzanite suite. *Pendant by Cynthia Renée Inc; photo by John Parrish.*

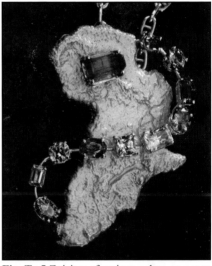

Fig. Tz.5 Zoisites of various colors on a map of Africa. *Pendant & photo: Frank Heiser.*

Fig. Tz.6 Pink zoisite (thulite)

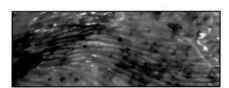

Fig. Tz.7 Green zoisite (anyolite)

Fig. Tz.8 Pink tanzanite. *Cut by Clay Zava of Zava Mastercuts; photo by Robert Weldon.*

Fig. Tz.9 Green tanzanite (5.45 cts). *Gem from Pala Intl; photo: Wimon Manorotkul.*

Topaz $Al_2(F,OH)_2SiO4$—aluminum fluorohydroxysilicate

November birthstone, imperial topaz—23rd wedding anniversary stone

Most topaz is light brown when mined and turns colorless after lengthy exposure to light or low heat. Otherwise, it tends to be pale blue. Yellow, orange and pink topaz are highly regarded. Good brilliance and hardness also add to their value. High-quality, yellow-orange topaz, for example, may retail for a few thousand dollars per carat whereas citrine quartz of similar color and quality sells for less than $75/ct. Due to the price difference, some sellers call citrine quartz, which is widely available, "quartz topaz" or even "topaz" to make it sound more expensive. Prior to the 18th century, all yellow stones were usually called "topaz." Even today, some miners refer to almost any yellow stone as a topaz. Therefore, when buying topaz, ask the seller to specify on the receipt that it is genuine topaz and not quartz or another gemstone.

The world's largest producer of topaz is the state of Minas Gerais in Brazil. For almost 300 years, its Ouro Preto district has supplied the world with yellow, orange and pink topaz. Other sources include Australia, Germany, Mexico, Myanmar, Pakistan, Russia, Sri Lanka, and the U.S. Crystals weighing several kilos are common.

RI: 1.61–1.64	SG: 3.50–3.57	Hardness: 8	Crystal System: Orthorhombic
Cleavage: Perfect in one direction		Optic Character: DR, biaxial positive	
Pleochroism: Weak to distinct trichroism		Reaction to Chemicals: Affected very slightly	

Toughness: Poor. Because of its perfect cleavage, stones can easily break, chip or form straight cracks when dropped or knocked. Topaz requires special care when being set.

Stability to Light: Natural brownish topaz may fade, especially some from Mexico, Utah and Siberia. Pink or blue varieties and yellow non-irradiated stones from Brazil are generally stable.

Care Tips: Avoid ultrasonics, steamers, strong heat, rough handling and rapid cooling or heating.

Treatments: Blue is usually irradiated & heated; pink, red, yellow and orange are usually heated; green is occasionally irradiated and commonly CVD coated. "Mystic topaz" is CVD-coated topaz.

Varieties

PINK to RED TOPAZ: Top-grade red or strong pink topaz is the most valuable color of topaz. The redder and more saturated the color, the rarer and more costly the stone, as much as $9000/ct retail. Natural-color pink stones, which generally come from Pakistan, can sell for more than those which are treated. Most pink topaz is heated brownish-yellow topaz from Brazil. Light purple-pink stones may look lavender.

GOLDEN YELLOW to ORANGE TOPAZ: When this variety is intensely colored and has reddish or pink overtones, it is called IMPERIAL TOPAZ and can retail from about $200 to more than $6000/ct. Stones that lack pink highlights or have a low color saturation are less valuable.

BLUE to BLUE-GREEN TOPAZ: Produced by irradiating and then heating certain colorless material, blue topaz can look like fine aquamarine, but most blue topaz is a deeper blue and looks less natural. Ever since the market was flooded with this topaz, its price has dropped to levels below $40/ct retail.

COLORLESS TOPAZ: Used to simulate diamonds, this is the least expensive and most plentiful topaz. It is often sold as WHITE TOPAZ, CLEAR TOPAZ or SILVER TOPAZ.

Fig. Tp.1 Natural color pink topaz from Katlang, Pakistan atop the remainder of the crystal from which it was cut. *Gem cut and photographed by Jeff White.*

Fig. Tp.3 Topaz from Minas Gerais Brazil. *Cut by John Dyer; photo by Priscilla Dyer.*

Fig. Tp.6 Imperial topaz. *Ring by Hubert Inc; photo by Diamond Graphics.*

Fig. Tp.2 Imperial topaz. *Ring by Hubert Inc; photo by Diamond Graphics.*

Fig. Tp.4 Blue topaz. *Ring and photo from Erica Courtney.*

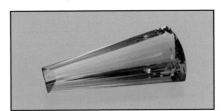

Fig. Tp.5 Bicolor topaz (13.35 cts). *Gem: Pala Intl; photo: Jason Stephenson.*

Fig. Tp.7 Lavender topaz from Minas Gerais Brazil. *Cut by John Dyer; photo: Priscilla Dyer.*

Tourmaline (a large group of mineral species, only a few of which are familiar gemstones) An October birthstone and 8th wedding anniversary stone

No other gem offers buyers a wider variety of colors than tourmaline. Besides being found in every color of the rainbow, tourmaline may also be multicolored in one piece.

It wasn't until the early 18th century that tourmaline was recognized as a distinct gemstone. Before then, the red and green varieties were often classified as a type of ruby or emerald. Then it was discovered that tourmaline possessed curious properties. When heated or pressed at one end, it became electrically charged; it could attract and repel lightweight, nonmetallic materials like ashes, dust and small bits of paper. In 1768, Linnaeus, a Swedish naturalist, suggested that green tourmaline was related to **schorl**, the black species of tourmaline which had been known for almost two centuries in Europe. The origin of the name "tourmaline" might be from the Sinhalese *turmali*, meaning a mixed parcel of unknown gems. A parcel of tourmaline was sent by mistake under this name to stone dealers in Amsterdam in 1703, and the name may have stuck.

Tourmaline has been found in significant quantities in Afghanistan, Brazil, California, Kenya, Maine, Madagascar, Mozambique, Nigeria, Pakistan, Russia, Sri Lanka, Tanzania and Zambia. Its properties are below:

RI: 1.62–1.65	**SG**: 3.00–3.26	**Hardness**: 7–7.5	**Cleavage**: None
Crystal System: Hexagonal (Trigonal)		**Optic Character**: DR, uniaxial negative	
Toughness: Fair; heat-treated stones may be more fragile than untreated stones			
Pleochroism: Moderate to strong, usually light and dark tones of the same body color			
Reaction to Heat: Strong heat may cause irradiated stones to fade.			
Stability to Light: Normally stable, but some irradiated stones may fade with prolonged exposure.			
Care Tips: Ultrasonics are risky. Avoid sudden temperature changes in order to prevent fracturing.			
Treatments: Heating—common; irradiation—common in red, pink & purple; fracture filling—sometime			

Varieties and Species

GREEN TOURMALINE: This variety is plentiful and comes in a wide range of shades. It tends to have a strong green dichroism that makes one direction of the stone (along the optic axis) appear darker than when viewed in other directions. To lighten and improve the color, green tourmaline is commonly heat-treated. Pastel green tourmaline is often called MINT TOUMALINE, especially if it is bluish. Stones that are brownish, blackish and yellowish are the least expensive. Those with an intense natural green color approaching the color of a good emerald cost the most.

Top-color green tourmalines are found in East Africa and are typically colored by chromium and/or vanadium. As a result, they're called CHROME TOURMALINES. Not all stones sold as "chrome tourmaline" contain chromium. To test for chromium content, look at the tourmaline through a color filter called a Chelsea filter. The stone will look reddish or pinkish instead of green if it contains chromium and/or vanadium.

Eye-clean green tourmaline is readily available. Therefore, good-quality stones are expected to have a high clarity. Top quality chrome tourmaline can retail for as much as $2500/ct. Most green tourmaline, however, is more affordable, with retail prices ranging from about $20/ct in very low qualities to $1500/ct in high-grade stones.

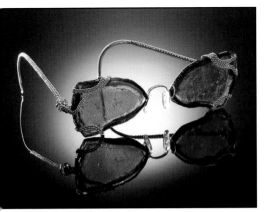

Fig. Tm.1 Nigerian watermelon tourmaline eyeglasses from John S. White. *Photo by Mark Mauthner.*

Fig. Tm.2 Tourmalines. *Multi slab necklace by Melissa Spencer; photo by Diamond Graphics.*

Fig. Tm.3 Multicolor tourmaline from California Himalaya mine. *Pala International / Mia Dixon.*

Fig. Tm.4 Chrome tourmaline from Tanzania (4.36 cts). *Pala International; photo by Mia Dixon.*

Fig.Tm.5 Mint tourmaline accented with diamonds and tsavorites. *Ring & photo from Suna Bros.*

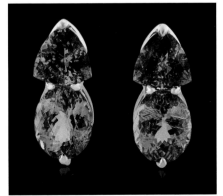

Fig. Tm.6 Brazilian Paraiba tourmaline. *Gems from Pala International; photo by Mia Dixon.*

Fig.Tm.7 Mozambique cuprian tourmaline. *Earrings by Cynthia Renée Inc; photo by Cristine Prisk.*

PINK or RED TOURMALINE: The discovery of pink tourmaline in southern California in 1898 helped popularize this stone. Red and pink tourmaline is also mined in Afghanistan, Brazil, Madagascar, Nigeria and Russia. RUBELLITE is a trade name applied to red and strong pink tourmaline. Tourmalines that are light pink or that look brownish-red under incandescent light generally sell for less than pure-red or hot pink tourmaline, all other factors being equal. High quality rubellite above one carat retails for about $500–$2000/ct.

Pink and red tourmalines are commonly irradiated and often heated to intensify their color. The stones are not radioactive and the color is relatively stable. However, strong heat like that from a display window or a jeweler's torch may cause the color to fade. The color will return if the stone is irradiated again. Sometimes rubellite is treated with fillers to improve its clarity.

BLUE-GREEN, GREEN-BLUE, BLUE TOURMALINE: If this tourmaline is from Africa and contains copper as a coloring element, it's called CUPRIAN TOURMALINE. If it's from the state of Paraíba in Brazil, it's PARAÍBA TOURMALINE, the most expensive and rare tourmaline. It has wholesaled at prices above $50,000/ct. Some trade members call any copper-bearing blue-green to green-blue tourmaline "paraíba tourmaline." Still other vendors apply the term to any green-blue tourmaline. Before paying high premiums for Paraíba tourmaline, ask sellers to define their meaning of the term, and ask for a lab report from a respected lab. Consult *Exotic Gems: Volume 3* by Renée Newman for in-depth information on Paraíba and other tourmalines.

INDICOLITE is a mineralogical term for tourmaline that has an indigo color or that is dark greenish or grayish blue. The color is often lightened with heat treatment.

YELLOW, ORANGE, BROWN or GOLDEN TOURMALINE: Yellow and orange tourmaline occur naturally but are sometimes produced by irradiating light yellow or green tourmaline. Heat can cause the resulting color to fade. Strong yellow tourmaline is especially prized because of its rarity. Brown tourmaline, tends to cost the least.

COLORLESS OR WHITE TOURMALINE: This tourmaline occurs naturally in the same areas as pink tourmaline. It's also produced by heating pale pink tourmaline.

BLACK TOURMALINE (Species name **SCHORL**): This is a common opaque stone which was widely used for mourning jewelry during the Victorian era in Britain. Today it is occasionally used instead of jet or chalcedony in inexpensive jewelry.

BICOLORED or MULTICOLORED TOURMALINE: The pink and green variety is the most common type, but stones can also be pink and colorless, blue and green or yellow and brown. Some stones have more than two colors. The most valued stones have distinct saturated colors with sharp boundaries and no fractures. Green and pink slices of crystal tourmaline that have concentric color banding are called WATERMELON TOURMALINE. Most of the multicolored tourmaline on the market is the tourmaline species ELBAITE. LIDDICOATITE, a much more rare tourmaline species, may also have pronounced color zoning. Madagascar is the most important producer of liddicoatite.

CAT'S-EYE TOURMALINE: This is found in a variety of colors but pink and green are less difficult to find than red or blue colors. Cat's-eye tourmaline is occasionally treated with epoxy fillers to improve transparency and seal the tubes causing the cat's-eye. The fillers prevent dirt from entering the tubes.

COLOR-CHANGE TOURMALINE: In daylight, this tourmaline may look yellowish to brownish green whereas under incandescent light it appears orangy red to brownish orange. Color-change tourmaline is rare and considered a collector's item.

Fig. Tm.8 Liddicoatite (5.41 cts). *Gem from Pala International; photo by Mia Dixon.*

Fig. Tm.9 Nigerian rubellite. *Cut by J. L. White Fine Gemstones; photo: Jeff White.*

Fig. Tm.10 "Autumn color" untreated tourmalines from Morogoro, Tanzania. *Gems from Advanced Quality Co. Ltd; photo by Kobi Sevdermish.*

Fig.Tm.11 Afghan tourmaline. *Gems cut by Clay Zava of Zava Mastercuts; photo by Robert Weldon.*

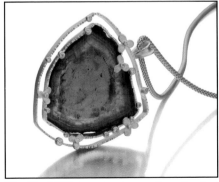

Fig. Tm.12 Watermelon tourmaline. *Pendant & photo from Barbara Heinrich Studio LLC.*

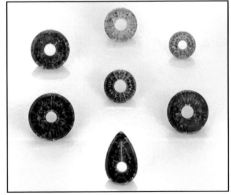

Fig. Tm.13 Color range of tourmalines from the Brazilian state of Paraiba. Note the high color saturation. All colors are natural except for that of the two heated greenish blue tourmalines at the top and top right. *TorusRings™ cut by Glenn Lehrer; photo by Robert Weldon.*

Turquoise $CuAl_6(PO_4)_4(OH)8 \cdot 5H_2O$—hydrated copper aluminum phosphate
December birthstone and 11th wedding anniversary stone

For more than 2000 years, northeastern Iran (aka Persia) has been a key source of high-grade turquoise. Persian turquoise made its way to Europe via Turkey, which is probably why by the 13th century, the French were calling it *pierre turquoise—Turkish stone*. China, Tibet, Mexico, India, the Sinai Peninsula and Southwestern USA have also been important producers.

Turquoise is the national gemstone of Iran. In Tibet, it has had a role comparable to that of jade in China. To the Aztecs, turquoise was a commodity more valuable than gold. According to the 17th century book *Gemmarum et Lapidum Historia* by Anselmus de Boot, turquoise was so highly regarded by European men, that no man considered his hand to be well adorned unless he wore a fine turquoise ring.

Unfortunately, a glut of imitation and reconstituted turquoise in modern times has lowered the prestige of what was for centuries a highly esteemed gem. Dyed magnesite and howlite are common imitations. Natural turquoise, however, is found in two forms: as rare tiny crystals or as a translucent to semi-opaque mass found as solid nodules or veinlets in rock. The properties of turquoise are given below:

RI: 1.61–1.65	**SG**: 2.40– 2.85	**Hardness**: 5–6	**Toughness**: Good to poor
Cleavage: None	**Pleochroism**: weak	**CS**: Triclinic	**Optic Char**: AGG (DR)

Reaction to Chemicals: May be discolored by perspiration, perfume, heavy liquids, cosmetics, lotions, soap and ultrasonic cleaning solutions. Dissolves very slowly in HCL.

Reaction to Heat: Much material will fracture, shatter, crackle and/or discolor, but some turquoise found in volcanic rock can withstand the heat of a flame.

Stability to Light: Untreated turquoise may fade or discolor depending on the source and material

Care Tips: Avoid ultrasonics, chemicals, steam and heat. Clean with warm soapy water.

Treatments: Porous material is commonly impregnated with resin, wax or plastic to deepen and stabilize the color; sometimes a colorant is added. **Zachary processed, turquoise** is treated with chemicals and then heated. Turquoise powder is frequently bonded with resin or silica compounds and called reconstituted, reconstructed or composite turquoise. The powder might not even be turquoise in stones sold as reconstituted turquoise. Crushed turquoise and charcoal may be bonded with epoxy and sold as Lander Blue turquoise.

When buying turquoise, assume it has been treated unless you are dealing with a knowledgeable, trustworthy seller who writes on the receipt "untreated natural turquoise." Lab reports from reputable labs with high-tech equipment will also indicate if the material is natural. Turquoise ranges in color from blue and blue-green to green. Stones sold as purple turquoises have been dyed.

Natural turquoise stones commonly contain portions of their matrix (host rock) or mineral inclusions. When they form weblike patterns, the material may be called "spider web turquoise." This turquoise is popular because it looks more natural than solid, evenly colored turquoise. Keep in mind that the patterns are not always natural; ink and shoe polish have been used to create a spiderweb-like appearance.

The most prized turquoise is untreated, non-processed, durable and stable and has a naturally attractive color. However, such turquoise is extremely rare.

Fig. Tq.1 Persian turquoise. *Jewelry by Zaffiro; photo by Elizabeth Gualtieri.*

Fig. Tq.2 Turquoise from the Burtis Blue Mine in Cripple Creek, Colorado. *Ring courtesy Burtis Blue Turquoise; Photo © Renée Newman.*

Fig. Tq.3 Dyed magnesite that was sold as turquoise. *Cabochons and bead lab samples from Stone Group Laboratories; photo by Cara Williams.*

Fig. Tq.4 Turquoise inlay from the now depleted Morenci Arizona Mine. *Ring by Different Seasons Jewelry; photo by Jessica Dow.*

Left: Fig. Tq.5 Materials often sold as turquoise—rectangular block: crushed aluminum phosphate and turquoise reconstituted with polymer, rounded rock at far right: aluminum phosphate colored by Ty-D-Bol blue liquid toilet bowl cleanser, oval cabochon: crushed turquoise, charcoal and epoxy. *Materials and information from Clint Cross and Louisa McKay of Burtis Blue Turquoise. Photo © Renée Newman.*

Zircon ZrSiO₄—Zirconium silicate, a December birthstone

Zircon is not the same as cubic zirconia (CZ). Zircon is natural zirconium silicate, a gemstone with exceptional brilliance and a diamond-like luster. Cubic zirconia is zirconium oxide, a synthetic stone with a different chemical composition. When colorless and well-cut, both stones resemble diamonds. Before CZ was introduced to the market in 1976, heat-treated, colorless zircon was widely used as a diamond imitation. Gemologists can easily distinguish zircon from CZ because of zircon's high double refraction, and from diamond because zircon is much softer.

Zircon comes in almost every color of the spectrum. Much of the zircon sold in jewelry stores is blue. This color results from heating brownish zircon. Before the 1900's, orange or reddish-brown zircon, called **hyacinth**, was the most common type. The name "zircon" may have originated from the Persian word *zargun* meaning gold-color. Three of the main sources of zircon are Cambodia, Thailand and Sri Lanka. It is also found in Vietnam, Myanmar, Tanzania, France and Australia. Bangkok is the world's cutting and marketing center for zircon.

There is a wide variation of optical and physical properties among zircons so mineralogists classify them into at least two types: those with low and those with high properties (RI above ≈1.90, specific gravity above ≈4.6, and a hardness of ≈7 1/2). Some zircons are an intermediate type. Zircon property ranges are given below:

RI: 1.78–2.01	**SG**: 3.9–4.8	**Hardness**: 6–7.5	**Crystal System**: Tetragonal
Cleavage: Imperfect and negligible		**Optic Character**: DR, Uniaxial positive	

Toughness: Untreated stones—fair to good; heated stones—poor to fair, chip and abrade easily

Pleochroism: Weak to moderate except in blue stones, where it's strong blue & brownish yellow to colorless.

Stability to Light: Some heat-treated stones may revert to their original color.

Care Tips: Ultrasonics are risky. Avoid strong light and heat; it can cause some stones to change color.

Treatments: Blue & colorless: routinely heated; other colors: often heated; fancy colors: occasional coating

Varieties

BLUE ZIRCON: It often resembles aquamarine and blue topaz but has more fire and brilliance. Blue zircon sold in jewelry stores is heat treated and susceptible to abrasions, especially when mounted in rings. Retail prices can range from $40-$800/ct.

GREEN ZIRCON: Found mostly in Sri Lanka, this zircon is often grayish or yellowish. It's not uncommon for street vendors to sell it as green tourmaline or green sapphire. A curious property of green zircon is that it usually emits some level of natural radioactivity. Retail prices generally range from about $40–$700/ct.

YELLOW, ORANGE & BROWN-RED ZIRCON: In their natural state, these zircons tend to be either brownish or pale. Heat treatment can intensify the color and reduce brown tints. To verify that the colors are stable, dealers sometimes expose them for several days to the sun. Retail prices range from about $40–$600/ct, depending on size and quality. Brown is the least expensive zircon color.

COLORLESS ZIRCON: This variety occurs rarely in nature, but can be produced by heating brownish zircon. Today, CZ has replaced colorless zircon as the most popular diamond imitation.

Fig. Z.1 Zircon from Tanzania. *Gemstones cut by Larry Woods of Jewels from the Woods and Shawn Maddox; photo by John Parrish.*

Fig. Z.2 Golden zircon. *Ring by Sarosi by Timeless Gems; photo: Diamond Graphics.*

Fig. Z.3 Blue zircon (5.67 cts tw). *Earrings by Cynthia Renée Inc; photo by Mogadham.*

Fig. Z.4 Red zircon (7.69 cts) from Tanzania. *Gem cut by Lisa Elser; photo: C. Tom Schlegel.*

Fig.Z.5 Tanzanian bicolor zircon (10.12 cts). *Cut and photographed by Clay Zava.*

Fig. Z.6 Sri Lankan green zircon (5.44 ct). *Gem from Coast to Coast Rarestones; photo: John Bradshaw.*

Fig.Z.7 Tanzanian yellow zircon (10.86 cts). *Cut and photographed by Clay Zava.*

Ammolite
A form of aragonite ($CaCO_3$) from fossilized ammonite, an extinct shellfish

Despite its ancient origins, ammolite, a multi-colored gemstone, is a relative newcomer to the gem market. First sold as a gem material in 1962, it wasn't until 1983 that major production began.

Originally discovered by the Blackfoot Indians, ammolite is mined only in Southern Alberta, Canada. Most ammolite is assembled into doublets or triplets to increase durability because solid ammolite is usually thin and fragile, If it's untreated and solid, ammolite is usually priced per carat and shaped as a freeform to maximize size. Depending on the quality and size, triplets can range in retail price from $20 to $2000 *per piece*. Solid treated ammolites are also priced by the piece.

Extra fine quality ammolites display three or more sharp, brilliant colors. The most prized stones are those that exhibit the full color spectrum including blue and purple, which are the rarest colors. Thick dividing lines and dull, grayish colors also lower the price. For a much more in-depth discussion of ammolite, consult *Exotic Gems, Vol. 1* by Renée Newman and the Spring 2001 issue of *Gems & Gemology*.

Ammolite. *Pendant: Leslie Weinberg; photo by Robert & Orasa Weldon.*

RI:1.525–1.67	SG: 2.75–2.84	Hardness: 3.5–4	Reaction to Chemicals: Attacked by acids
Stability to Light: Stable		**Stability to Heat**: breaks down and loses iridescence; avoid heat	

Toughness: Red ammolite is relatively tough, but blue and purple are brittle. Triplets with quartz or synthetic spinel tops are more durable.

Care Tips: Avoid ultrasonics, rough wear, heat and chemicals. Clean with damp soft cloth.

Treatments: Much of it is impregnated with an epoxy type substance to increase durability. It's *not* heat treated or irradiated.

Ammolite. *Brooch/pendant & photo from Korite Intl.*

Ammonite—the fossilized shellfish that is the source of ammolite. *Pendant by Zaffiro; photo by Elizabeth Gualtieri.*

Andalusite Al_2SiO_5—aluminum silicate (pronounced an′ dl oo′ site)

Andalusite is sometimes called "poor man's alexandrite" because it may appear green, red and yellow when viewed from different directions. (In technical terms, it has strong pleochroism.) Its face-up color is typically a brownish or yellowish green to orangy brown. Andalusite was named after the Spanish province of Andalusia, where it was first found. Today its primary sources are Brazil and Sri Lanka. Fine, transparent stones above 3 carats retail for as much as $700/ct. Stones from 1--3 carats range from about $20–$300/ct. See *Exotic Gems, Volume 2* for more info.

RI: 1.63–1.64	SG: 3.13–3.20	Hardness: 6.5–7.5	Reaction to Heat: stable
Stability to Light: stable		Reaction to Chemicals: none	Toughness: fair to good
Care Tips: Ultrasonic cleaning is usually safe for andalusites with good clarity.			
Treatments: Usually none. Heating produces a pink color from some green stones but is rarely done.			

Apatite $Ca_5(PO_4)_3$ (F, OH, Cl)$_3$, (A mineral group)

Apatite occurs in many shades of yellow, green, blue, pink, purple, violet, and colorless as well as in cat's-eye form. It has become popular because some of the blue and green colors resemble those of the highly prized Paraiba tourmaline. Blue to green transparent apatite retails from about $25– $400/ct depending on quality and size. Yellow apatite is more common and costs less. Because of its rarity, purple apatite from Maine costs the most, as much as $1000/ct.

RI: 1.63–1.65	SG: 3.13–3.23	Hardness: 5	Toughness: Fair
Stability to Light: usually stable, some pink may fade		Optic Char: DR, uniaxial negative,	
Care Tips: Ultrasonics are risky. Avoid acids, high heat & rough wear; wash with warm soapy water.			
Treatments: Often heated and occasionally coated or irradiated. Fracture filling is possible.			

Left: Madagascar apatites (24.90 ct tw) & diamonds. *Earrings by Leslie Weinberg; photo by Robert & Orasa Weldon.*

Andalusite (3.11 cts) from Pala International. *Photo by Mia Dixon*

Azurite $Cu_3(CO_3)_2(OH)_2$—Copper carbonate hydroxide (pronounced azh′er rite′)

Azurite derives its name from the Persian *lazhward*, meaning "blue" in reference to its striking blue to violet color ranging from deep to light. It is usually translucent to semiopaque, but it can also be transparent. Azurite has been used as a pigment for paint and dyes; however, the color is not stable over time. A unique characteristic of azurite is that it can gradually turn into malachite through oxidation. Most azurite on the market is intermixed with malachite, and is called **azurmalachite**. Solid blue azurite, though rare, is available as cabochons, druse and faceted stones.

RI: 1.730-1.846	**SG**: 370–3.89	**Hardness**: 3.5–4	**Toughness**: poor
Care Tips: Avoid ultrasonics, steam cleaners, chemicals, acids and high heat.			
Treatments: May be impregnated with resins or wax to improve polish and hide cracks			

Benitoite $BaTiSi_3O_9$—barium titanium silicate (pronounced ben nee′toe-ite′)

Benitoite is a popular item among gem collectors because of its rarity, high brilliance, diamond-like fire and appealing natural blue color. It was named after San Benito County, California where it was discovered in 1906. Since gem-quality benitoite is mined only in that state, it was selected as the Official State Gemstone of California in October of 1985.

Benitoites over two carats are rare and can retail for more than $10,000/ct if you're able to find them. One- to two-carat stones may range from $1000–$7000 depending on size and quality. For benitoites under one carat, retail prices are about $300–$5000/ct. The benitoite mine is closed to commercial production.

RI:1.757–1.804	**SG**: 3.61–3.68	**Hardness**: 6–6.5	**Toughness**: fair
Pleochroism: strong blue/colorless dichroism		**Optic Character**: DR, uniaxial positive	
Stability: Stable to light, sensitive to high heat		**Treatments**: usually untreated, rarely heated	
Care Tips: Ultrasonics are risky. Avoid acids & rapid temperature changes. Warm, soapy water is safe.			

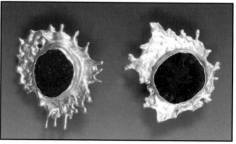

Left: Benitoite jewelry from Paul Cory of Iteco Inc. *Photo by Jeff Scovil.*

Azurite earrings. *Created and photographed by Carina Rossner.*

Calcite CaCO₃—Calcium carbonate

Common worldwide, calcite is the main component of marble. Mexico, Russia, Canada, Iceland, and the US are sources of transparent yellow and colorless calcite. Spain and Zaire are the sources of a pink to purple calcite variety called **cobaltocalcite**. Other colors include red, orange, yellow, green and blue. Calcite is soft (3 on the Mohs scale) and breaks easily when hit.

Even though calcite gems are not common, calcite is an abundant mineral found throughout the world. It's also a component of pearls and shells, which are used for carvings, beads and cabochons.

RI: 1.486–1.658	**SG**: 2.58–2.75	**Hardness**: 3	**Toughness**: Poor in single crystals
Care Tips: Avoid ultrasonics, steamers, rough wear, chemicals and high heat.			
Treatments: commonly impregnated with wax or plastic to improve polish appearance; occasionally irradiated to produce blue, yellow or lavender from white marble, but irradiated color may fade; calcite marble is commonly dyed and the dyes may fade.			

Charoite A rock composed of charoite (calcium, potassium silicate) and other minerals

Charoite is a lovely stone with variegated purple, lavender and white patterns and sometimes crystals of orange, gray and black. It was probably discovered in the 1940's during extension work on the Trans-Siberian Railroad in the Charo River area of Russia; hence the name. It's only source to date is the Sakha Republic. Typically used for carvings, charoite is also cut into beads and cabochons.

RI: 1.548–1.561	**SG**: 2.54–2.78	**Hardness**:5–6	**Toughness**: fair
Care Tips: Avoid ultrasonics. Steamer is risky. Clean with warm soapy water.			
Treatments: Commonly impregnated with wax or polymers to improve appearance & durability			

Calcite and cobaltocalcite. *Gems from Pala International; photo by Mia Dixon.*

Charoite. *Pendant by Revelations in Stone; photo by Arriana Larmony.*

Danburite $CaB_2(SiO_4)_2$ — calcium borosilicate

Named after Danbury, Connecticut where it was first reported in 1839, most danburite is colorless and has been mined in Mexico since the late 1950's. It is a bright, durable gemstone, usually of high clarity, that can be worn with anything and it's available in sizes as large as 15 carats or more. Madagascar is the main source of brownish yellow danburite. The gem is also found in Myanmar, Tanzania and Russia.

RI: 1.63-1.64	SG: 2.97–3.03	Hardness: 7–7.5	Toughness: good
Care Tips: Ultrasonics and steamers are risky. Clean with warm soapy water			
Treatments: Usually none, but some Russian material is irradiated to intensify color			

Untreated yellow danburite (3.98 ctts) from Tanzania. *Cut & photographed by Clay Zava of Zava Mastercuts.*

Colorless danburite (4.24 cts) from Mexico. *Cut and photo by Clay Zava..*

Diaspore AlO(OH) — aluminum oxide hydroxide (pronounced DYE a spore)

Diaspore, whose color ranges from light green to yellow, tan, gray or pinkish, was discovered in the Ural Mountains in Russia in 1801. Transparent color-change diaspore was found in the Aydin Mugla district, Turkey, in 1977 and to date, it is still the only commercial source of color-change diaspore. **Zultanite** is a trademarked name for transparent color-change diaspore.

RI: 1.69–1.75	SG: 3.3–3.5;	Hardness: 6.5–7	Optic char: DR biaxial +
Care Tips: Avoid ultrasonics, steamers, heat & acids. Clean with warm soapy water			
Treatments: Normally none, but fracture filling is possible			

Left: Color change in Zultanite— pastel yellowish green in daylight to pale pink in low wattage incandescent light and candlelight. *Zultanites and photo courtesy Zultanite Gems LLC.*

Diopside CaMgSi$_2$O$_6$ — Calcium magnesium silicate (pronounced dye op′ side)

The best-known diopside variety is **chrome diopside**, which is deep green and found mainly in Russia and Kenya. Retail prices range from about $40–$250/ct. Black star diopside is mined in India and usually has four rays, but may have six. Other diopsides may be colorless, pale green, brown and in rare cases blue or violet.

RI: 1.66–1.72	SG: 3.22–3.38	Hardness: 5.5–6.5	Toughness: fair to poor
Care Tips: Avoid ultrasonics, rough wear & jeweler's torch. Clean with warm soapy water.			
Treatments: Normally none except for possible fracture filling			

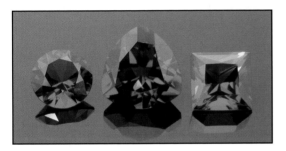

Left: Chrome diopside from Russia. *Gems and photo courtesy Columbia Gem House.*

Fluorite (formerly called fluorspar) CaF$_2$ — Calcium fluoride

The name "fluorite" comes from the Latin *fluere,* which means "to flow," since it melts easily and is used as a flux in the smelting of metals. The word "fluorescence" was in turn derived from fluorite because it was one of the first fluorescent minerals ever observed. Natural and synthetic fluorite occur in a wide range of colors, including purple, pink, yellow, green and blue. It may also be multicolored or display a color change. Fluorite is popular because of its diversity, affordability and its supposed metaphysical properties as an aid to objectivity, balance and concentration.

RI: 1.43–1.44	SG: 3.0–3.25	Hardness: 4	Toughness: poor
Care Tips: Avoid chemicals, jeweler's torch, ultrasonics, steamers, high heat & rough wear.			
Treatments: Commonly heat treated, often impregnated with resin to strengthen it, sometimes irradiated to produce a violet color from colorless material			

Fluorites. *Gems from Pala, International; photo by Mia Dixon.*

Fluorite. *Cabochons from Jone-Gems; photo © Renée Newman.*

Gaspéite: (Ni,Mg,Ca,Fe)CO₃ — nickel, magnesium, calcium, iron carbonate

Accepted as a separate mineral in 1966, gaspéite was named after the Gaspé Peninsula in Quebec, Canada, where it was discovered around nickel sulfide deposits. It's a translucent to semiopaque, yellowish-green stone that often contains brown inclusions. Finds in Australia north of Perth have increased its availability. Today, it is not uncommon to visit a specialty store, Indian shop or Southwestern US designer gallery and see gaspéite mounted in silver jewelry, strung as beads or cut as figurines. Prices are relatively low. Cabochons are available for less than $100.

RI: 1.61–1.83	SG: 4.5–5	Hardness: 4.5–5	Toughness: fair to poor
Care Tips: Avoid ultrasonics and steamers. Clean in warm soapy water.			
Treatments: may be impregnated with a polymer, wax or plastic			

Hematite F₂O₃ — Iron oxide

Hematite has a metallic luster and is typically opaque with a dark gray to black color. When faceted, it resembles a black diamond because of its bright luster. When scratched or scraped it produces a characteristic reddish powder, which was used as a pigment for Egyptian cave paintings, American Indian face paint and American barns. The name "hematite" is derived from the Greek *hema* (blood) since the color of the stone's powder (streak) resembled dried blood. Major deposits are in Australia, Brazil, Canada, China, Russia, South Africa, Venezuela and the United States.

One variety that has become popular with designers is **rainbow hematite** from Minas Gerais, Brazil. It has an attractive iridescence resulting from a thin film of aluminum phosphate on its surface. Hematite is normally not treated.

RI: 2.94–3.22	SG: 5.00–5.28	Hardness: 5.5–6.5	Toughness: good to excellent
Care Tips: Ultrasonics and steamers are safe. May become magnetic when heated.			

Left: Gaspéite. *Pendant & photo by Carina Rossner.*

Hematite cufflinks from Lang Antiques, San Francisco. *Photo courtesy Lang Antiques.*

Kyanite Al₂SiO₅ — aluminum silicate (pronounced KYE a nite)

Al_2SiO_5

Most kyanite is similar in color to blue sapphire and it often has a fibrous appearance. Its name is derived from the Greek *kyanos,* meaning "blue." Though kyanite is normally blue, it may also be green, yellow, orange, brown, gray, white or colorless and it can range from transparent to semiopaque. The finest quality kyanite is found in Nepal. Brazil, China, India, Mozambique, Myanmar, Tanzania and the United States are other sources. More detailed information is in *Exotic Gems, Volume 2* by Renée Newman.

RI: 1.71–1.73	SG: 3.53–3.70	Hardness: 4–5 & 6–7.5	Toughness: fair to poor
Care Tips: Avoid ultrasonics and steamers. Clean in warm soapy water.			
Treatments: Normally none, but some material is heated and fracture filling is possible.			

Larimar NaCa₂Si₃O₈(OH) — sodium calcium silicate hydroxide

$NaCa_2Si_3O_8(OH)$

If you ever go on a Caribbean cruise, you'll probably see larimar jewelry for sale. Larimar is a variety of the mineral species pectolite found in the Dominican Republic. It has a blue to bluish-green color, often mottled with white, and its transparency ranges from semitransparent to semiopaque. The name was given to the stone by a Dominican, Miguel Méndez, combining his daughter's name LARIssa and MAR, the Spanish word for sea. Larimar is used by some people as a healing stone associated with the thymus and thyroid glands. The color of larimar is natural and not the result of treatment.

RI:1.59–1.63	SG: 2.75–2.88	Hardness: 4.5–5	Toughness: fair
Care Tips: Avoid ultrasonics, acids and the heat of a jeweler's torch.			

Kyanite. *Photo © Henry A. Hänni.*

Larimar. *Pendant and photo by Diana March of Jewels of the Earth.*

Kyanite earrings. *Photo © Renée Newman.*

Maw-sit-sit A chromium-rich rock composed of kosmochlor, chromite, chrome jadeite, symplectite, chrome-amphibole or amphibole, and a mixture of minor minerals

Maw-sit-sit is a rare green rock, usually mottled with spots, swirls and veins that are black, various shades of green and sometimes white. The appearance varies depending on the mineral content. First identified in 1963 by Swiss gemologist Eduard J. Gübelin, it was named after the small village of Maw-sit-sit in northwestern Myanmar (Burma) near the area that is still the only source of the material. In addition to being sold as cabochons and freeforms, maw-sit-sit is carved and cut as beads.

RI:1.52–1.74	SG: 2.5–3.2	Hardness: 6	Toughness: good
Care Tips: Ultrasonics and chemicals are risky. Reaction varies with mineral content.			

Natural Glass Mainly SiO_2 — silicon dioxide (e.g., obsidian and moldavite)

Obsidian is a natural glass that forms when very siliceous lava with low water content cools very quickly. Most of the material used in jewelry is from North America. Obsidian usually has a black, brown or gray body color. It may be banded, exhibit a golden or silver sheen, or have white snowflake-like patterns. **Rainbow obsidian** is an iridescent, untreated variety found in Mexico and Oregon.

Natural glasses that are formed from the impact of meteorites are called **tektites**. They're named after the locality in which they're found. **Moldavite**, the best known tektite, is from the Moldau River area of Czechoslovakia and is typically yellowish to brownish green and often transparent.

RI:1.48–1.51	SG: 2.33–2.50	Hardness: 5-5.5	Toughness: fair to good
Care Tips: Ultrasonic cleaning is usually safe, but avoid high heat and rough wear.			

Maw-sit-sit. *Stone Group Labs / Cara Williams.*

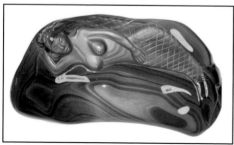

Mexican obsidian. *Carving from Opalos Romero; photo by Juan José Virgen.*

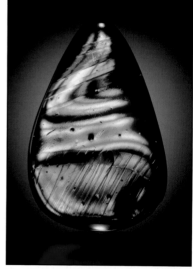

Fire (rainbow) obsidian from Oregon. *Emory Coons; photo by Jeff Scovil.*

Phenakite Be_2SiO_4 — beryllium silicate (FEN a kite), also called "phenacite"

If you'd like an affordable diamond substitute that is bright, durable, and completely natural, consider buying a phenakite. Although it can be pink, light yellow, brownish, or white, much of the phenakite entering the market now is colorless and transparent. It was named in 1833 from the Greek *phenak* for "deceiver" because it was often mistaken for quartz. Sources include Brazil, Colorado (USA), Madagascar, Myanmar, Namibia, Nigeria and Russia. It's usually untreated and can be cleaned in ultrasonics.

RI: 1.654–1.670	SG: 2.95–3.00	Hardness: 7.5–8	Toughness: good

Prehnite $Ca_2Al_2Si_3O_{10}(OH)_2$+Fe — Calcium aluminum silicate

Most prehnite is translucent and green to yellowish green, but it may also be semi-transparent to transparent (very rare) and yellow, orange, brown, gray, white, colorless or in rare cases pink. Some fibrous material is cut to show a cat's-eye effect. First discovered in South Africa by Dutch mineralogist Colonel Henrik Von Prehn (1733-1785), prehnite was the first mineral known to be named after a person.

RI: 1.61-1.64	SG: 2.8–2.95	Hardness: 6–6.5	Toughness: fair to good
Care Tips: Avoid ultrasonics, steam cleaners, acids and high heat.			
Treatments: Occasionally impregnated with wax or polymers, fracture filling is possible.			

Phenakite (6.15 cts). *Ring by Gordon Aatlo; photo by Kelly Allen.*

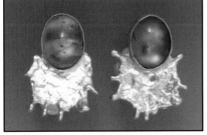

Prehnite. *Earrings and photo by Carina Rossner.*

Prehnite and aquamarine. *Necklace by Zaffiro; photo by Elizabeth Gualtieri.*

Psilomelane (BaH$_2$O)$_2$Mn$_5$O$_{10}$, — Barium and manganese hydrous oxide

Psilomelane (sil LAHM uh lane) is a black opaque rock which offers designers distinctive designs and textures. Some psilomelane cabs have a surface crust covered by tiny black sparkling crystals, which is called **druse**. Unlike black onyx or black quartz druse, which is dyed, psilomelane has a natural jet black color. Sources include Mexico, Brazil, Canada, England, Germany and the U.S. Clean in warm soapy water.

SG: 4.6–4.72	**Hardness**: 5–6	**Fracture**: Uneven	**Toughness**: good
Treatments: Normally none; fracture filling and titanium coating are possible.			

Rhodochrosite MnCO$_3$—Manganese carbonate (row′ duh crow′ site)

Rhodochrosite, whose name means "rose coloring" in Greek, can have either a solid pink to red to orange color, or may be variegated and banded with different shades of pink resembling agate banding. The banded material is translucent to semiopaque, and most of it is found in Argentina. Much of the material is carved into ornamental figurines; some of it is used for cabochons or beads.

In 1974 South Africa became an important source of translucent to transparent solid-color rhodochrosite but commercial production in South Africa has ceased. The Sweet Home mine in Alma, Colorado has produced much of the world's finest rhodochrosite. Other sources have included Brazil, Canada, Peru and China. As of this writing, there is no commercial mining of rhodochrosite, only scattered finds.

RI: 1.578–1.840	**SG**: 3.4–3.7	**Hardness**: 3.5–4.5	**Toughness**: fair
Care Tips: Avoid ultrasonics, steam cleaners, acids and high heat.			
Treatments: Occasionally heat treated, fracture filling is possible			

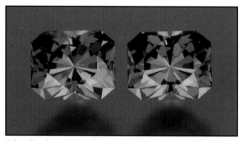

Rhodochrosite. *Cut and photo by Jeff White.*

Psilomomelane. *Inlay pendant by Mark Anderson of Different Seasons Jewelry; photo by Jessica Dow.*

Rhodochrosite stalactite. *Cabochon from Iteco Inc; photo by Jeff Scovil.*

Rhodonite $MnSiO_3$ (+Ca) — Manganese silicate

Rhodonite is usually pink with veins or patches of black manganese oxide and is translucent to semiopaque. A few rare specimens are red and transparent. Aggregate material is more durable than the transparent type. Rhodonite is found in Australia, Russia, Sweden, India, Canada, Mexico, South Africa, Tanzania, the U.S. and Japan.

RI: 1.72–1.75	SG: 3.50–3.76	Hardness: 5.5–6.5	Toughness: poor to good
Care Tips: Ultrasonics & steamers are risky. Avoid acids, jeweler's torch & rough wear.			
Treatments: Sometimes impregnated and/or dyed; fracture filling is possible.			

Seraphinite $H_8Mg_5Al_2Si_3O_{18}$, magnesium, aluminum, silicate hydroxide

Seraphinite is a trade name for a distinctive forest green variety of clinochlore variegated with silvery chatoyant fibers. The name was derived from the Hebrew word *seraph* (a celestial being with three pairs of wings) in reference to its feathery wing patterns. Seraphinite comes from the Korshunovskaia Mine near Baikal Lake in Eastern Siberia Russia. The mineral clinochlore was found and described by Russian mineralogist Niolai Kokasharov (1818–1892).

RI: 1.571–1.599	SG: 2.55–2.75	Hardness: 2–2.5	Toughness: poor to fair
Care Tips: Ultrasonics & steamers are risky. Avoid acids, jeweler's torch and rough wear.			
Treatments: Often impregnated with wax or polymers to improve polish and durability			

Rhodonite box with Russian hallmarks auctioned 12-14-2000 by Christie's East. Hammer price: $3,878. *Photo from Gail Levine of www.AuctionMarketResource.com.*

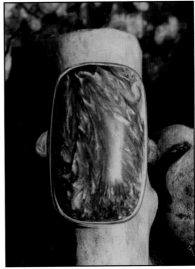

Seraphinite. *Ring by Revelations in Stone; photo by Arriana Larmony.*

Rhodonite. *Coast-to-Coast Rare Stones Intl.*

Serpentine (Mg,Fe,Ni)$_3$Si$_2$O$_5$(OH) — magnesium silicate hydroxide

Serpentine is a common jade substitute; it's actually a group of rock-forming minerals with a similar chemical composition but different properties. Like nephrite and most jadeite, serpentine stones are typically rocks composed of more than one mineral. It is commonly light to dark yellowish green, although it may also be yellow, green, bluish green, gray, brown or black. Its name comes from the word "serpent" because it often resembles the skin of a snake. Most serpentine is translucent to semiopaque, but it may also be semitransparent and faceted. **Bowenite**, the most valuable serpentine, is a highly translucent to semitransparent variety of serpentine with a hardness ranging from 4 to 5.5. It's sometimes sold under the misnomers of "new jade" or "Korean jade."

RI: 1.553–1.574	**SG**: 2.35–2.65	**Hardness**: 2.5–5.5	**Toughness**: fair

Care Tips: Avoid ultrasonics, solvents, jeweler's torch and high heat.

Treatments: May be dyed and/or impregnated with wax or polymers

Sodalite Na$_8$Al$_6$Si$_6$O$_{24}$Cl$_2$ — a complex sodium aluminum silicate chloride

Named in 1811 for its sodium content, sodalite is usually dark blue to violet-blue with white and sometimes yellow or red veining. It is typically semiopaque to translucent but can also be transparent and colorless or light blue, thanks to discoveries of new deposits. Much sodalite resembles lapis lazuli; in fact sodalite is a component of lapis lazuli, but sodalite rarely contains pyrite inclusions. In addition, sodalite is more translucent than lapis lazuli and has a lower density. Sources include British Columbia, Ontario, Russia, India, Germany, Italy, Norway, Bolivia and the U.S.

Hackmanite is a pink or purple variety of sodalite that is transparent to translucent and often has a unique property called **tenebrescence**; it either fades to colorless when exposed to light or it becomes darker after exposure to SW UV lighting.

RI: 1.480–1.487	**SG**: 2.15–2.30	**Hardness**: 5.5–6	**Toughness**: fair to good

Care Tips: Avoid ultrasonics, solvents, jeweler's torch and high heat.

Treatments: Sometimes fracture filled with oil or Opticon; occasionally dyed

Serpentine. *Courtesy International. Gemological Services; photo by Sindi Schloss.*

Sodalite. *Earrings by Amy Kahn Russell; photo by Noelle Fuecht.*

Sphalerite ZnS — zinc sulfide (SFALer ite)

Sphalerite is a lively, brilliant gem that is usually yellow, orange or red and has three times the fire of a diamond. Gem-grade material is also occasionally green or bicolored, showing, for example, both yellow and orange face-up. A chief ore of zinc, most sphalerite is industrial quality, and translucent to near opaque with a dark brown or black color due to iron in its chemical makeup. Unfortunately, it is very fragile because of its low hardness and six directions of perfect cleavage. Therefore, don't wear sphalerite in a ring; instead, display its beauty in a pendant or earrings.

RI: 2.37-2.43	SG: 3.90–4.10	Hardness: 3.5–4	Toughness: poor
Care Tips: Avoid ultrasonics, steamers, jeweler's torch and high heat.			

Sphene (Titanite) $CaTiSiO_5$ — Calcium titanium silicate (SFEEN)

If you'd like a green or yellow stone that is as brilliant as a diamond and has more fire, then sphene is the right gem for you. Sphene is noted for its high dispersion (fire, sparkles of rainbow colors). If the stone is colored by chromium, it can have an almost emerald-like green color; chrome-green sphenes fetch the highest prices. In addition to its usual colors of green, yellowish green and yellow, sphene may also be brown or orange. The only disadvantage with sphene is that it can chip easily, so it is best to limit its use in rings for dressy occasions instead of everyday wear. Madagascar is the largest producer, but sphene is also found in Brazil, Mexico, India, Pakistan, Sri Lanka, Myanmar, Switzerland, Austria, Afghanistan, Russia, Namibia, Canada and the U.S.

RI: 1.85–2.05	SG: 3.4–3.6	Hardness: 5–5.5	Toughness: fair
Care Tips: Ultrasonics are risky. Avoid steamers, acids, rough wear & high heat.			
Treatments: Brown sphene may be heat-treated to produce orange or reddish brown color.			

Sphalerite. *Pala International / Mia Dixon.*

Sphene. *Cut & photo: Clay Zava.*

Sphalerite. *Pala International / Mia Dixon.*

Sphene. *Richard Krementz Gemstones.*

Sugililte (K, Na)(Na, Fe)$_2$(Li$_2$Fe)Si$_{12}$O$_{30}$ — sodium potassium lithium silicate

a complex silicate colored by manganese and often mixed with chalcedony (quartz)

Most sugilite used in jewelry has a striking purple to magenta color and ranges from translucent to semiopaque. It can also be yellow-brown, violet, pink, or black. The greater the translucency and the more intense and uniform the purple color, the more valuable the gem. Sugilite was named for petrologist Ken-ichi Sugi, who discovered the mineral in Japan in 1944. However, the first commercial sugilite deposit was not found until 1979 in the Wessels mine near Hotazel, South Africa during mining operations for manganese ore. Sugilite has also been reported in India, Canada and Italy.

RI: 1.60–1.61	**SG**: 2.69–2.79	**Hardness**: 5.5–6.5	**Toughness**: good
Care Tips: Ultrasonics are risky, warm soapy water is safe			
Treatments: sometimes dyed or stabilized with wax or polymers			

Vesuvianite (Idocrase) Ca$_{10}$(Mg,Fe)$_2$Al$_4$(SiO$_4$)$_5$(Si$_2$O$_7$)$_2$(OH)$_4$, calcium magnesium iron aluminum silicate hydroxide

Vesuvianite was discovered in the 18th century in Naples, Italy at Mount Vesuvius, hence the name given by the German mineralogist Abraham Werner. French mineralogist René Haüy preferred to call it "idocrase," which comes from the Greek words *idos* and *krasis* meaning mixed appearance because idocrase crystals resemble those of other minerals. Both names are still used today, but mineralogists usually call the mineral vesuvianite, and consider "idocrase" a synonym.

Transparent green to green-yellow vesuvianite is currently the most widely available variety of this mineral. Magadi, Kenya has the highest commercial production of the material. Another variety of vesuvianite, which is bright green to yellow-green and translucent to semi-opaque, is named **californite**.

RI: 1.70–1.72, spot 1.71	**SG**: 3.3–3.5	**Hardness:** 6.5	Toughness: fair to good
Care Tips: Clean in warm soapy water, ultrasonics are risky			
Treatments: Normally none except for possible fracture filling			

Sugilite. *Pendant by Barbara Westwood; photo by Sky Hall.*

Sugilite. *Pala Intl / Mia Dixon.*

Vesuvianite. *Earring by Amy Kahn Russell / Noelle Feucht.*

12

Caring for Your Gems

Cars, furniture and clothing look better and last longer if you take care of them. The same is true of gems. Clothing manufacturers sew written instructions into their products. They'll say, for example, "dry clean only," "cool iron," etc. It's not possible to place this kind of information on gems. Therefore, you must rely on salespeople, brochures and books for instructions on how to look after your gems and jewelry.

It's important to realize that colored gemstones are not as durable as diamonds. Diamonds are used as drills, they're boiled in acid, they're heated and then plunged in water. Don't treat colored gems in this manner. Many gems are very susceptible to **thermal shock**—sudden temperature changes. These include emerald, garnet, kunzite, opal, peridot, quartz, tanzanite, topaz and tourmaline. You should not, for example, lay in the sun and then jump in a swimming pool while wearing these gems, nor should you go from a hot tub to a cold shower. If you do, the sudden temperature change could possibly cause the stones to crack or shatter.

With some stones, you should avoid heat in general. These include amethyst, emerald, kunzite, malachite, opal, red tourmaline and turquoise. Don't leave these gems sitting on a sunny window sill or wear them to the beach. The heat might make amethyst, kunzite and red tourmaline fade and it could dry out and discolor the fillings in emerald. It could also cause small cracks in some malachite, opal and turquoise.

Malachite and turquoise are unusually sensitive to chemicals. Ammonia and acid solutions as well as everyday products such as perfumes and lotions can harm them. Pickling solutions used by jewelers and some acids will etch the surface of peridot. Solvents such as alcohol and acetone will gradually dissolve the fillers in emeralds and other oiled or filled stones. Dyed lapis, dyed jade and other dyed stones are also adversely affected by solvents. Chlorine can gradually pit and dissolve gold alloys. The pitting can also occur while swimming or while soaking in a hot tub with chlorine.

The safest way to clean a gemstone is to wash it in lukewarm water using a mild liquid soap or detergent that contains no ammonia. Then dry it with a soft, lint-free cloth. If the dirt can't be washed off with a cloth, try using a toothpick or a Water Pik to remove it. If that doesn't work, have it professionally cleaned. Jewelers often clean stones with ultrasonic cleaners, which send high frequency sound waves through solutions. The vibrating fluid removes built-up dirt, but it can also shake poorly-set stones from their mountings and damage some types of gems. The table on the next page indicates which stones should not be cleaned in ultrasonics. Much of the data in the chart is from the GIA *Gem Reference Guide*.

Ultrasonic cleaners should also be avoided with the following types of stones:
♦ Badly flawed stones of any species—they can be further damaged by ultrasonic cleaning.
♦ Oiled and/or dyed stones—the oil and dye may be removed, often quickly.
♦ Stones with glass-filled cavities—the filling may fall out.
♦ Any kind of fracture-filled stone, including diamond. The cleaning solution or vibration could cause the fillings to gradually cloud, discolor or be removed.

Gemstone	Safe for Ultrasonics?	Comments
Aquamarine	Usually safe	Ultrasonics are risky if liquid inclusions or fractures are present
Chalcedony	Use caution	Chemicals may attack dyed stones
Chrysoberyl	Usually safe	
Diamond	Usually safe	Ammonia, acids and repeated ultrasonic cleaning may damage some fracture fillings
Emerald	Avoid	Avoid heat and solvents like acetone and alcohol
Garnet	Use caution	Avoid thermal shock; ultrasonics are risky if liquid inclusions or fractures are present
Iolite	Risky	Avoid acids and thermal shock
Jade	Avoid if jade is waxed &/or dyed	Acids can affect polish on stones. Avoid solvents. Most jade is waxed.
Kunzite	Avoid	Avoid heat and strong light to prevent fading
Lapis lazuli	Avoid	Avoid acids, acetone and other solvents
Malachite	Avoid	Avoid chemicals and heat
Moonstone	Avoid	Avoid heat
Opal	Avoid	Avoid thermal shock, high heat & chemicals
Peridot	Use caution	Avoid acids and pickling solutions
Quartz	Use caution	Avoid thermal shock
Ruby & sapphire	Depends on the stone	Avoid ultrasonics with stones that are oiled, fractured or filled with lead glass.
Star ruby & sapphire	Risky	Avoid ultrasonics with black star sapphires and with oiled or dyed stones
Spinel	Usually safe	
Tanzanite	Avoid	Avoid thermal shock
Topaz	Avoid	Avoid thermal shock
Tourmaline	Risky	Avoid thermal shock
Turquoise	Avoid	Avoid heat and chemicals
Zircon	Risky	Avoid thermal shock

Some stones are more susceptible to knocks and bumps than others. This is because of their easy cleavage (ability to split along certain crystal planes). Kunzite, tanzanite, iolite, topaz and feldspars such as moonstone and sunstone all fit in this category. If these gems are knocked lightly just right at a specific angle against a wall or furniture, they can sometimes crack. Diamonds also cleave, but it normally takes a hard blow or lots of pressure to create diamond cleavage. Therefore, don't assume that a tanzanite or a topaz can withstand the same abuse as a diamond. You must treat them with much more care.

The most durable colored stones are jade, ruby, sapphire, chrysoberyl and spinel. Jade is softer than many gems, but its toughness (resistance to chipping, breaking and cracking) surpasses all other gem materials, including diamond. The other stones listed in the table can also provide good wear. Just treat them as you would a fine silk scarf or any other accessory.

Storing Your Jewelry

When you store jewelry, protection from theft and damage should be a prime consideration. A jewelry box can protect pieces from damage if they are stored individually, but it is one of the first places burglars look when they break into a home. So it's best to reserve jewelry boxes for costume jewelry when they are displayed on tables or dressers.

Jewelry pieces should be wrapped separately in soft material or placed individually in pouches or the pockets of padded jewelry bags. If a piece is placed next to or on top of other jewelry, the metal mountings or the stones can get scratched. Use your imagination to find a secure place in your house to hide jewelry pouches, bags and boxes. If expensive jewelry is seldom worn, it's best to keep it in a safe deposit box.

Miscellaneous Tips

♦ Avoid wearing jewelry (especially rings) while participating in contact sports or doing housework, gardening, repairs, etc. In fact, it's a good idea to take most colored-stone jewelry off when you come home and change into casual clothes. If during rough work you want to wear a ring for sentimental reasons or to avoid losing it, wear protective gloves. However, even gloves won't offer full protection.

♦ Occasionally check your jewelry for loose stones. Shake it or tap it lightly with your forefinger while holding it next to your ear. If you hear the stones rattle or click, have a jeweler tighten the prongs.

♦ Don't remove rings by pulling on any of their gemstones. Instead grasp the metal ring portion. This will help prevent the stones from coming loose and getting dirty.

♦ When you set jewelry near a sink, make sure the drains are plugged or that the piece is put in a protective container or on a spindle. Otherwise, don't remove the jewelry.

♦ Clean your jewelry on a regular basis. Once a week is not too often for a ring that is worn daily. Risky cleaning procedures can be avoided by regular cleaning.

♦ About every six months, have a jewelry professional check your ring for loose stones or wear and tear on the mounting. Many stores will do this free of charge, and they'll be happy to answer your questions regarding gem care. Jewelers want you to enjoy the jewelry you purchase from them. You will as long as you take good care of it.

Birthstones & Anniversary Stones

Birthstones established in 1912 by the American National Retail Jewelers' Association:

January	Garnet	July	Ruby
February	Amethyst	August	Peridot & sardonyx
March	Aquamarine & bloodstone	September	Sapphire
April	Diamond	October	Opal & tourmaline
May	Emerald	November	Topaz
June	Pearl or moonstone	December	Turquoise, lapis lazuli tanzanite & zircon

Anniversary Stones

1. Gold
2. Garnet
3. Pearl
4. Blue topaz
5. Sapphire
6. Amethyst
7. Onyx
8. Tourmaline
9. Lapis lazuli
10. Diamond
11. Turquoise
12. Jade
13. Citrine
14, Opal
15. Ruby
16. Imperial topaz & peridot
17. Amethyst
18. Garnet
19. Aquamarine
20. Emerald
23. Blue sapphire
25. Silver
26. Blue star sapphire
30. Pearl
35. Coral & Emerald
39. Cat's eye
40. Ruby
45. Alexandrite & sapphire
50. Gold
52. Star ruby
55. Alexandrite & emerald
60. Diamond

Astral Stones

Aquarius (January 22–February 21)	Garnet
Pisces (February 22–March 21)	Amethyst
Aries (Bloodstone–April 20)	Bloodstone
Taurus (April 21–May 21)	Sapphire
Gemini (May 22–June 21)	Agate
Cancer (June 22–July 22)	Emerald
Leo (July 23–August 22)	Onyx
Virgo (August 23–September 22)	Carnelian
Libra (September 23–October 23)	Peridot
Scorpio (October 24–November 21)	Aquamarine
Sagittarius (November 22–December 21)	Imperial Topaz
Capricorn (December 22–January 21)	Ruby

Gemstones in the Order of their Descending Mohs Hardness

Gemstone	Hardness	Gemstone	Hardness	Gemstone	Hardness
Diamond	10	Epidote	6–7	Azurite	3.5–4
Ruby	9	Tanzanite	6–7	Cuprite	3.5–4
Sapphire	9	Unakite	6–7	Malachite	3.5–4
Alexandrite	8.5	Zoisite	6–7	Phosphosiderite	3.5–4
Chrysoberyl	8.5	Amazonite	6–6.5	Sphalerite	3.5–4
Taaffeite	8–8.5	Andesine	6–6.5	Coral	3–4
Spinel	8	Benitoite	6–6.5	Howlite	3–3.5
Topaz	8	Labradorite	6–6.5	Calcite	3
Aquamarine	7.5–8	Marcasite	6–6.5	Serpentine	2.5–5.5
Beryl	7.5–8	Moonstone	6–6.5	Pearl	2.5–4.5
Bixbite	7.5–8	Nephrite	6–6.5	Lepidolite	2.5–4
Phenakite	7.5–8	Prehnite	6–6.5	Gold	2.5–3
Emerald	7.5–8	Pyrite	6–6.5	Silver	2.5–3
Dumortierite	7–8.5	Amblygonite	6	Chrysocolla	2–4
Almandine	7–7.5	Maw-sit-sit	6	Amber	2–2.5
Danburite	7–7.5	Orthoclase	6	Seraphinite	2–2.5
Pyrope	7–7.5	Sugilite	5.5–6.5		
Rhodolite	7–7.5	Hematite	5.5–6.5		
Spessartine	7–7.5	Opal	5.5–6.5		
Tourmaline	7–7.5	Rhodonite	5.5–6.5		
Uvarovite	7–7.5	Actinolite	5.5–6		
Amethyst	7	Haüyne	5.5–6		
Ametrine	7	Scapolite	5.5–6		
Citrine	7	Sodalite	5.5–6		
Jeremejevite	7	Tugtupite	5.5–6		
Rose Quartz	7	Bronzite	5.5		
Smoky Quartz	7	Enstatite	5.5		
Tiger's-eye	7	Moldavite	5.5		
Andalusite	6.5–7.5	Charoite	5–6		
Grossular	6.5–7.5	Diopside	5–6		
Spessartine	6.5–7.5	Hypersthene	5–6		
Tsavorite	6.5–7.5	Lapis lazuli	5–6		
Andradite	6.5–7	Psilomelane	5–6		
Chalcedony	6.5–7	Turquoise	5–6		
Demantoid	6.5–7	Brazilianite	5–5.5		
Zircon	6–7.5	Obsidian	5–5.5		
Agate	6.5–7	Sphene (titanite)	5–5.5		
Axinite	6.5–7	Apatite	5		
Diaspore	6.5–7	Hemimorphite	5		
Hiddenite	6.5–7	Smithsonite	5		
Jadeite	6.5–7	Gaspéite	4.5–5		
Jasper	6.5–7	Larimar	4.5–5		
Kornerupine	6.5–7	Scheelite	4.5–5		
Kunzite	6.5–7	Kyanite	4–7.5		
Peridot	6.5–7	Variscite	4–5		
Sinhalite	6.5–7	Platinum	4–4.5		
Spodumene	6.5–7	Ammolite	4		
Tiger's eye	6.5–7	Fluorite	4		
Zultanite	6.5–7	Rhodochrosite	4		
Vesuvianite	6.5	Magnesite	3.5–4.5		
Sillimanite	6–7.5	Aragonite	3.5–4		

Gemstones in the Order of their Descending Refractive Index

Hematite	2.94–3.22	Smithsonite	1.621–1.850	Sodalite	1.48
Cuprite	2.848–2.850	Prehnite	1.616–1.649	Hackmanite	1.48
Diamond	2.417–2.419	Tourmaline	1.614–1.666	Chrysocolla	1.460–1.570
Sphalerite	2.369–2.43	Hemimorphite	1.614–1.636	Glass	1.44–1.90
Scheelite	1.918.–1.937	Gaspéite	1.61–1.83	Fluorite	1.43–1.44
Sphene	1.88–2.05	Turquoise	1.610–1.650	Opal	1.37–1.52
Demantoid	1.841–1.887	Topaz	1.609–1.643		
Melanite	1.88–1.94	Sugilite	1.602–1.611		
Uvarovite	1.798–1.864	Brazilianite	1.60–1.623		
YAG	1.833	Nephrite	1.600–1.627		
Zircon	1.810–2.024	Larimar	1.59–1.64		
Spessartine	1.774–1.814	Howlite	1.583–1.608		
Almandine	1.78–1.830	Rhodochrosite	1.578–1.840		
Mali garnet	1.762–1.841	Amblygonite	1.578–1.646		
Ruby	1.762–1.778	Seraphinite	1.571–1.599		
Sapphire	1.762–1.778	Emerald	1.57–1.60		
Benitoite	1.757–1.804	Aquamarine	1.567–1.590		
Malaya garnet	1.75–1.78	Red beryl	1.564–1.574		
Rhodolite	1.75–1.795	Variscite	1.56–1.59		
Chrysoberyl	1.746-1.763	Serpentine	1.551–1.574		
Alexandrite	1.746–1..763	Labradorite	1.559–1.572		
Grossular	1.73–1.770	Charoite	1.548–1.561		
Hessonite	1.73–1.75	Amethyst	1.544–1.553		
Epidote	1,729–1.768	Citrine,	1.544–1.553		
Azurite	1.730 1.846	Rock crystal	1.544–1.553		
Pyrope	1.714–1.75	Rose quartz	1.544–1.553		
Taaffeite	1.718–1.724	Smoky quartz	1.54–1.55		
Rhodonite	1.72–1.75	Andesine	1.543–1.557		
Spinel	1.712–1.762	Iolite (Cordierite)	1.542–1.578		
Kyanite	1.710–1.734	Jasper	1.54		
Vesuvianite	1.70–1.72	Amber	1.539–1.545		
Diaspore	1.69–1.75	Ivory	1.535–1.570		
Tanzanite	1.691–1.700	Pearls	1.53–1.69		
Phosphosiderite	1.69–1.74	Aragonite	1.525–1.685		
Dumortierite	1.678–1.723	Lepidolite	1.53–1.556		
Axinite	1.674–1.704	Agate	1.53–1.54		
Hypersthene	1.673–1.731	Chalcedony	1.53–1.54		
Diopside	1.66–1.72	Chrysoprase	1.53–1.54		
Kornerupine	1.660–1.699	Amazonite	1.514–1.539		
Hiddenite	1.660–1.681	Sunstone	1.525 1.548		
Kunzite	1.660–1.681	Unakite	1.52–1.76		
Sillimanite	1.657–1.680	Ammolite	1.52–1.68		
Malachite	1.655–1.909	Maw–sit–sit	1.52–1.74		
Jadeite	1.652–1.688	Moonstone	1.518–1.532		
Peridot	1.650–1.703	Magnesite	1.515–1.717		
Enstatite	1.66–1.75	Lapis lazuli	1.50		
Phenakite	1.650–1.670	Tugtupite	1.496–1.502		
Apatite	1.63–1.655	Haüyne	1.494–1.505		
Jeremejevite	1.630–1.653	Calcite	1.486–1.658		
Andalusite	1.63–1.65	Moldavite	1.48–1.51		
Danburite	1.630–1.636	Obsidian	1.48–1.5		

Gemstones in the Order of their Descending Density (Specific Gravity)

Platinum (pure)	21.4	Enstatite	3.2–3.5	Serpentine	2.44–2.62
Gold (pure)	19.3	Tanzanite	3.2–3.4	Variscite	2.42–2.58
Silver (pure)	10.49	Diopside	3.2–3.4	Haüyne	2.4–2.5
Cuprite	6.00–6.15	Gaspéite	3.21–3.70	Tugtupite	2.36–2.57
Scheelite	5.90–6.12	Apatite	3.16–3.23	Obsidian	2.35–2.50
Sugilite	5.5–6.5	Hiddenite	3.15–2.21	Moldavite	2.32–2.38
Zircon	5.5–5.9	Kunzite	3.15–2.21	Turquoise	2.31–2.84
Hematite	5.00–5.28	Sillimanite	3.14–3.25	Sodalite	2.15–2.30
Pyrite	4.85–5.10	Andalusite	3.13–3.23	Hackmanite	2.15–2.35
Marcasite	4.85–4.92	Amblygonite	2.98–3.06	Opal	1.98–2.50
YAG	4.55	Fluorite	3.00–3.25	Chrysocolla	1.90–2.45
Psilomelane	4.4–4.72	Magnesite	3.00–3.12	Ivory	1.70–2.0
Spessartine	4.1–4.2	Danburite	2.97–3.03	Jet	1.19–1.35
Smithsonite	4.3–4.65	Phenakite	2.95–2.97	Amber	1.05–1.09
Ruby	3.97–4.05	Brazilianite	2.94–3.00		
Sapphire	3.95–4.03	Aragonite	2.93–2.97		
Zircon	3.93–4.73	Nephrite	2.9–3.03		
Almandine	3.8–4.25	Tourmaline	2.82–3.32		
Sphalerite	3.9–4.1	Prehnite	2.8–2.95		
Rhodolite	3.85	Lepidolite	2.8–3.3		
Pyrope	3.7–3.8	Ammolite	2.75–2.84		
Uvarovite	3.7–3.81	Larimar	2.75–2.90		
Demantoid	3.7–4.1	Sugilite	2.69–2.79		
Melanite	3.7–4.1	Aquamarine	2.68–2.80		
Azurite	3.70–3.89	Emerald	2.67–2.80		
Chrysoberyl	3.7–3.78	Red beryl	2.66–2.70		
Hessonite	3.64–3.69	Labradorite	2.65–2.75		
Benitoite	3.61–3.69	Andesine	2.65–2.69		
Taaffeite	3.6–3.62	Amethyst	2.65		
Tsavorite	3.57–3.73	Citrine	2.65		
Spinel	3.54–3.63	Onyx	2.65		
Kyanite	3.53–3.70	Rock crystal	2.65		
Phosphosiderite	3.5–4.0	Rose quartz	2.65		
Rhodonite	3.50–3.76	Aventurine	2.64–2.69		
Diamond	3.50–3.53	Sunstone	2.62–2.65		
Topaz	3.49–3.57	Pearl	2.6–2.85		
Grossular	3.4–3.8	Coral	2.60–2.70		
Rhodochrosite	3.4–3.7	Agate	2.60–2.64		
Sphene (titanite)	3.4–3.6	Pietersite	2.6		
Hypersthene	3.4–3.5	Jasper	2.58–2.91		
Vesuvianite	3.3–3.5	Calcite	2.58–2.75		
Epidote	3.3–3.5	Iolite (Cordierite)	2.58–2.66		
Hemimorphite	3.3–3.5	Moonstone	2.54–2.63		
Diaspore	3.3–3.5	Amazonite	2.56–2.58		
Jadeite	3.30–3.38	Unakite	2.55–3.20		
Peridot	3.28–3.48	Seraphinite	2.55–2.75		
Kornerupine	3.28–3.35	Charoite	2.54–2.78		
Dumortierite	3.26–3.41	Maw–sit–sit	2.5–3.2		
Axinite	3.26–3.36	Lapis Lazuli	2.50–3.00		
Malachite	3.25–4.10	Howlite	2.45–2.71		

Bibliography

Books, Booklets & DVDs

Arem, Joel. *Color Encyclopedia of Gemstones.* New York: Chapman & Hall, 1987.

Bauer, Dr. Max. *Precious Stones Volume II.* New York: Dover Publications: 1968, English translation first published in 1904.

CIBJO *Gemstone Book*, Bern, Switzerland. World Jewellery Confederation, 2013.

Cody, Andrew & Damien. *The Opal Story, A Guidebook.* Melbourne: Andrew & Damien Cody, 2008.
Cody, Andrew. *Australian Precious Opal.* Melbourne. Andrew Cody Party Ltd, 1991.

Cram, Len. *Beautiful Yowah & Koroit: Special Edition.* Lightning Ridge, Len Cram,
Cram, Len. *Beautiful Opals Australia's National Gem.* Lightning Ridge: Len Cram, 1999.

Crowe, Judith. *The Jeweler's Directory of Gemstones.* Buffalo, NY: Firefly Books, 2006.

Dedeyne, Roger & Quintens, I. *Tables of Gemstone Identification.* Belgium: Glinico-Ghent, 2007.

Deer, W. A., Howie. R. A., Zussman, J. *An Introduction to the Rock-Forming Minerals: Second Edition.* Essex, England: Longman Scientific & Technical, 1992.

Dennis, Daniel. *Gems, A Lively Guide for the Casual Collector.* New York: Harry Abrams, 1999.

Dominy, Geoffrey & Hammid, Tino, M, *Handbook of Gemmology,* Vancouver, BC: Amazonas Gem Publications, 2013.

Downing, Paul. *Opal Identification and Value.* Tallahassee: Majestic Press, 1992.

Eckert, Allan. *The World of Opals.* New York: John Wiley & Sons, Inc., 1997.

ExtraLapis, *Beryl No 7.* East Hampton, CT: Lapis International. 2005.
ExtraLapis, *Emeralds of the World, No 2.* East Hampton, CT: Lapis International. 2002.
ExtraLapis No. 11, *Garnet: Great Balls of Fire.* East Hampton, CT: Lithographic, LLC. 2008.
ExtraLapis No. 9, *Opal the Phenomenal Gemstone.* East Hampton, CT: Lithographic, LLC. 2007.
ExtraLapis No. 14, *Topaz: Perfect Cleavage.* East Hampton, CT: Lithographic, LLC. 2011.
ExtraLapis, *Tourmaline No 3.* East Hampton, CT: Lapis International. 2002.

Fang, Gu and Hongjuan Li, *Chinese Jade The Spiritual and Cultural Significance of Jade in China,* New York: Better Link Press, 2013.

Gemological Institute of America. *Gem Reference Guide.* Santa Monica, CA: GIA, 1988.

Grande, Lance, & August, Allison. *Gems & Gemstones.* Chicago: Univ. of Chicago Press, 2009.

Gubelin, Eduard J. *The Color Treasury of Gemstones.* New York: Thomas Y. Crowell, 1984.

Gubelin, Eduard J. & Koivula, John I. *Photoatlas of Inclusions in Gemstones, Volume 3.* Basel: Opinio Publishers, 2008.
Gubelin, Eduard J. & Koivula, John I. *Photoatlas of Inclusions in Gemstones, Volume 2.* Basel: Opinio Publishers, 2005.
Gubelin, Eduard J. & Koivula, John I. *Photoatlas of Inclusions in Gemstones.* Zurich: ABC Edition, 1986.

Gump, Richard. *Jade: Stone of Heaven.* Garden City, NY: Doubleday & Co, 1962.

Hall, Cally. *Eyewitness Handbooks, Gemstones.* London: Dorling Kindersley, 1994.
Hall, Cally. *Gems & Precious Stones,* Edison, NJ: Chartwell Books Inc., 1998.

Hodgkinson, Alan, *Gem Testing Techniques.* Scotland: Valery Hodgkinson, 2015.

Hoover, D B. *Topaz.* Oxford: Butterworth-Heinemann Ltd, 1992.

Hughes, Richard W. *Corundum*. London: Butterworth-Heinemann, 1990
Hughes, Richard W. *Ruby & Sapphire*, Boulder, CO: RWH Publishing, 1997.
Hughes, Richard W. *Ruby & Sapphire: A Collector's Guide*. Bangkok: Gem & Jewelry Institute of Thailand, 2014

Hurrell, Karen & Johnson, Mary L. *Gemstones*. New York: Metro Books, 2008.

Keverne, Roger. *Jade*. London: Aquamarine, 2010.

Kunz, George Frederick. *The Curious Lore of Precious Stones*. New York: Bell, 1989.
Kunz, George Frederick. *Gems & Precious Stones of North America*. New York: Dover, 1968.

Liddicoat, Richard T. *Handbook of Gem Identification*. Santa Monica, CA: GIA, 1989.

Matlins, Antoinette L. & Bonanno, A. *Jewelry & Gems: The Buying Guide*. South Woodstock, VT: Gemstone Press, 1993.

Miller, Anna M. *Gems and Jewelry Appraising*. New York: Van Nostrand Reinhold, 1988.

Nassau, Kurt. *Gemstone Enhancement, Second Edition*. London: Butterworths, 1994.

Newman, Renée. *Exotic Gems, Volume 1*, Los Angeles: Intl. Jewelry Publications, 2010.
Newman, Renée. *Exotic Gems, Volume 2*, Los Angeles: Intl. Jewelry Publications, 2011.
Newman, Renée. *Exotic Gems, Volume 3*, Los Angeles: Intl. Jewelry Publications, 2014.
Newman, Renée. *Exotic Gems, Volume 4*, Los Angeles: Intl. Jewelry Publications, 2016.
Newman, Renée. *Gem & Jewelry Pocket Guide*. Los Angeles: Intl. Jewelry Publications, 2015.
Newman, Renée. *Gemstone Buying Guide*. Los Angeles: Intl. Jewelry Publications, 2012.
Newman, Renée, *Rare Gemstones*, Los Angeles: Intl. Jewelry Publications, 2012.

O'Donoghue, Michael, Joyner Louise. *Identification of Gemstones*. Oxford, Butterworth-Heinemann, 2003.
O'Donoghue, Michael. *Synthetic, Imitation & Treated Gemstones*. Oxford: Butterworth-Heinemann, 1997.

O'Leary, Barry. *A Field Guide to Australian Opals*. Melbourne, Gemcraft Books, 1977

Read, Peter G. *Gemmology*. Oxford: Butterworth-Heineman, 1996.

Rubin, Howard. *Grading & Pricing with GemDialogue*. New York: GemDialogue Co., 1986.

Sauer, Jules Roger. *Brazil: Paradise of Gemstones*. Rio de Janeiro: Jules Roger Sauer, 1982.

Schumann, Walter. *Gemstones of the World*. New York: Sterling, 1997.

Sinkankas, John. *Van Nostrand's Standard Catalogue of Gems*. New York: Van Nostrand Reinhold, 1968.
Sinkankas, John. *Gemstone & Mineral Data Book*. Prescott, AZ. Geoscience Press, 1988.

Sisk, Gerald D. *Guide to Gems & Jewelry*. Knoxville, TN: Jewelry Television, 2011.

Sofianides, Anna & Harlow, George. *Gems & Crystals from the American Museum of Natural History*. New York: Simon & Shuster, 1990.

Themelis, Ted. *Gems & Mines of Mogok*. Thailand, Ted Themelis, 2008.

Thomas, Arthur. *The Gemstones Handbook*. UK: New Holland Publishers, 2008.

Wallis, Keith, *Gemstones: Understanding, Identifying, Buying*. Woodbridge, Suffolk: Antique Collectors Club, 2011.

Webster, Robert. *Gems, Fourth Edition*. London, Butterworths,1983.

White, John S. *The Smithsonian Treasury Minerals and Gems*. Washington D.C.: Smithsonian Institution Press, 1991.

Wise, Richard. *Secrets of the Gem Trade*. Lenox, MA: Brunswick House Press, 2003.

Zeitner, June Culp, *Gem & Lapidary Materials*. Tucson, AZ: Geoscience Press, 1996.

Zucker, Benjamin. *How to Buy & Sell Gems: Everyone's Guide to Rubies, Sapphires, Emeralds & Diamonds*. New York: Times Books, 1979.

Periodicals

Auction Market Resource for Gems & Jewelry. P. O. Box 7683 Rego Park, NY, 11374.
Australian Gemmologist. Brisbane: Gemmological Association of Australia.
Canadian Gemmologist. Toronto: Canadian Gemmological Association.
Gems & Jewellery. London: Gemmological Association of Great Britain.
Gems and Gemology. Santa Monica, CA: Gemological Institute of America.
The GemGuide. Glenview, IL: Gemworld International, Inc.
InColor: New York: ICA (International Colored Gemstone Association).
Jewellery Business. Richmond Hill, ON: Kenilworth Media, Inc.
Jewelers Circular Keystone. Radnor, PA: Chilton Publishing Co.
Jewelry News Asia. Hong Kong: CMP Asia Ltd.
Jewellery Review. Hong Kong: Brilliant Art Group.
Journal of Gemmology, London: Gemmological Association Great Britain.
Lapidary Journal Jewelry Artist. Loveland, CO: Interweave Press.
Rock & Gem. Ventura, CA: Miller Magazines, Inc.
Rocks & Minerals. Philadelphia: Taylor and Francis Group.
Southern Jewelry News. Greensboro, NC: *Southern Jewelry News*.

Miscellaneous: Courses, Brochures, Newsletters & PowerPoint

AGIL Fei Cui Jadeite Jade Smart Grading System.Asian Gemmological Institute & Laboratory
Gem A Diploma in Gemmology Course, 2009.
Gemological Institute of America Gem Identification Course.
Gemological Institute of America Gem Identification Lab Manual.
Gemological Institute of America Colored Stones Course.
Gornitz, Vivien; Schumate, Anna; Portnoy, Mitch. "The Three Faces of Jade" PowerPoint.
Mason-Kay "Guide to Natural Vs. Treated Jade"
Mason-Kay "Jadeite Information."
Bulletins of the New York Mineralogical Club.

Informational Websites Used for This Book

www.agta.org/gemstones/agta-gim.pdf
www.cibjo.org
www.friendsofjade.org
www.galleries.com
www.geminterest.com
www.gemlab.co.uk
www.gemologyonline.com
www.gemstone.org
www.gemstonemagnetism.com
www.geology.com
www.gia.edu
www.irocks.com
www.jtv.com
www.jtv.com/library/gemstone-chart.html
www.minerals.net
www.palagems.com
www.palaminerals.com
www.mindat.org
www.ruby-sapphire.com
www.wikipedia.org

Index

Other Books by RENÉE NEWMAN
Graduate Gemologist (GIA)

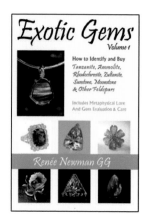

Exotic Gems, Volume 1

This is the first in a series of books that explores the history, lore, evaluation, geographic sources, and identifying properties of lesser-known gems. *Exotic Gems, Volume 1* has detailed info and close-up color photos of mounted and loose tanzanite, labradorite, zultanite, rhodochrosite, sunstone, moonstone, ammolite, spectrolite, amazonite andesine, bytownite, orthoclase and oligoclase.

"Chapters including 'Price factors in a nutshell' will prove indispensable to novice buyers. The breadth of information on each stone, Renee's guide to choosing an appraiser, 288 vibrant photos and a bibliography also make this book a handy resource for seasoned collectors." *Bead & Button*

"The great thing about any Renee Newman guide is that she writes for everyone - the professional jeweler, gemologist and hobbyist will all be able to glean important information and inspiration from her books." *Robyn Hawk, "Reading it All"*

154 pages, 288 color photos, 6" x 9", ISBN 978-0-929975-42-9, US$19.95

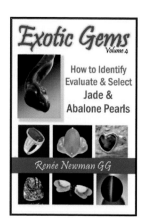

Exotic Gems, Volume 4
How to Identify, Evaluate & Select Jade & Abalone Pearls

"This book will help you pick your way through the jade minefield. Newman begins with a look at why jade was so highly valued by diverse cultures around the world, of which the Chinese were preeminent. She carefully explains the two true jades (nephrite and jadeite) as well as their less common confusing cousins: omphacite, kosmochlor, and maw-sit-sit. The long list of jade imitators is well covered and illustrated. Relevant gemological instruments are introduced and discussed . . . The quality factors for jadeite are well explained and illustrated . . . Jade sources and cultures are next described, with individual chapters for China, Burma, Guatemala, Canada (today's top source of nephrite), and the several USA jade sources . . . One last chapter covers secondary locales . . . An extra treat is a chapter on abalone pearls, a subject rarely written about. Newman covers what they are, where they are found, and how they are cultivated, as well as price factors and how to care for them. As in Newman's previous gemstone books the coverage is thorough and the writing clear. The numerous photographs are exceedingly helpful . . . If you have any interest at all in jade as a gemstone, Renée Newman's latest book is a must-have."

Eric Hoffman, Owner, Far East Gallery

136 pages, 338 color photos, 6" x 9", ISBN 978-0-929975-50-4, US$19.95

For more information, see **www.reneenewman.com**

Exotic Gems, Volume 2

Explores the history, evaluation, geographic sources, and identifying properties of alexandrite, andalusite, chryso-beryl cat's-eye, kyanite, common opal, fire opal, agatized dinosaur bone and garnets.

"This is the second in a series of books, boasting an amazing 408 color photographs depicting not only of gems mounted in jewellery but also loose gems, gems in the rough and gem beads! There are also diagrams and tables to aid in identification and evaluation. Six entire chapters are devoted to garnets, two chapters on common opal and even a chapter on dinosaur gembone! Also included are alexandrite, andalusite, chrysoberyl cat's-eye and kyanite.

. . . those familiar with Newman's previous books will recognise the **in depth, yet understandable** style, catering to professionals and lay people alike . . . Imparting a wealth of information on gemstone evaluation, as usual, with tips on detecting imitations, synthetics and gem treatments, Newman always entertains with interesting anecdotes of history, geographic sources and metaphysical lore of gems. Be ready to be informed and entertained."

The Australian Gemmologist, reviewed by Carol Resnick

154 pages, 408 color photos, 6" x 9", ISBN 978-0-929975-45-0, US$19.95

Exotic Gems, Volume 3

This volume discusses how to identify, evaluate, select and care for matrix opal, fire agate, blue chalcedony and all varieties of tourmaline. A chapter on Paraiba tourmaline is included.

"The simple genius in Renee Newman's Exotic Gems series is that no books like them have been written. What follows in *Volume Three*, as with its predecessors, is **a wholly comprehensive look at specific varieties of gems** not commonly featured in jewelry store cases."

Jeweler's Ethics Association

"One of the most noteworthy aspects of Newman's many gem-related books is her use of photographs to illustrate quality and showcase modern designs that effectively and beautifully utilize the materials. Details on locality, treatment of material, and care tips are always well researched. *Exotic Gems, Vol. 3* belongs in the library of gem and jewelry appraisers as **a quick and easy reference to the relative value factors of the stones** discussed, and is also relevant for those who are lovers of unusual gem materials."

Gems & Gemology, reviewed by Jo Ellen Cole

"A great reference . . . The quality of the photographs and their individual reference information listed can also be a great asset to an appraiser; helping locate possible comparison gemstones, designers, and/or gemstone dealers." *Naja Appraiser*

137 pages, 422 color photos, 6" x 9", ISBN 978-0-929975-48-1, US$19.95

For more information, see **www.reneenewman.com**

Other Books by RENÉE NEWMAN
Graduate Gemologist (GIA)

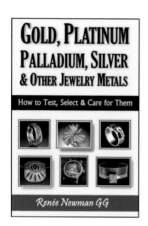

GOLD, PLATINUM PALLADIUM, SILVER & OTHER JEWELRY METALS

How to Test, Select & Care for Them

Renée Newman GG

Gold, Platinum, Palladium
Silver & Other Jewelry Metals
How to Test, Select & Care for Them

"Everything you didn't know about the jewellery metals gold, platinum, palladium, silver, copper, bronze, brass, iron, stainless steel, titanium, niobium, aluminum, tungsten carbide and cobalt chrome is included in this book. As a gemmologist I found this information most useful bridging the gaps in the jewellery knowledge that is usually not covered in gemmology. It also opens your eyes to look differently at metals you would not normally consider as jewellery metals. Typical of Newman's books, is the proliferation of luscious photographs and excellent tables – an inspiration for any jeweller. It is also **packed with technical information that can be referred to time and again.** Not to mention the fascinating tidbits of information, such as surgical instruments initially being made of silver due to their bacteria killing properties . . . The easy reading and beautiful photographs typical of all Newman's books make this one not only a reference book, but also an inspiration to consider buying and using metals not normally considered for use in jewellery." *The Australian Gemmologist,* reviewed by Carol Resnick

"You have managed to include a tremendous amount of very useful information on a very expansive and potentially dry subject, while staying **concise, interesting and even entertaining**. Honestly, I learned a great deal about metals I did not know - so much so that this book will now be with me on the job at all times as a primary reference." Dan Kapler, Refining Sales Manager, David H. Fell & Company, Inc.

"Each of your books fulfills a real need, and you perform the rare magical act of identifying with your reader, never talking down or assuming. Incredibly informative. . . . As always, the presentation is impeccable, photos, text, **clear and succinct**. I loved the tables of alloy composition, and enjoyed the tour behind an appraiser's methods." Eve Alfillé, Eve Alfillé Gallery in Evanston, IL

"What **a fascinating book**! I've been in the jewelry business since 1972 and yet even with all that experience, your book provided new insights." Chris Booth, Exotica Jewelry, Clarkdale, AZ

"An excellent and **comprehensive** guide to everything concerning the metals used in jewelry design. It is written clearly and concisely and has an abundance of charts and color photographs. It is not excessively technical yet it covers the topics thoroughly." *The Jewelry Appraiser,* reviewed by Kate Pearce

"You have put together a well-crafted tome. Your book is **very informative & easy to read & understand.** You have obviously done your research & clearly know much more about metallurgy than the average person in the industry, certainly more than I know! Kudos!!!" Lee J. Thompson, Jewelers Refining Group, Inc., New York City, NY

136 pages, 253 color photos, 6" x 9", ISBN 978-0-929975-47-4, US$19.95

Rare Gemstones

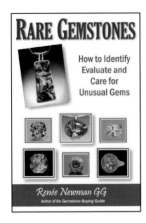

Provides concise information on the identification properties, geographic sources, treatments, imitations, durability, uses, value factors and pricing of non-traditional gems. High quality photos show the different colors, cutting styles and varieties of each gem and give ideas on how each can be used creatively in jewelry.

"*Rare Gemstones* is **a fascinating insight into the latest and more unusual gemstones that** are now finding their way into designer jewellery . . . over 60 of the lesser-used gem materials have been selected, documented and presented in a highly visual way . . . Where this book differs from others is in the extensive use of photographs of rough, cut and fashioned gemstones, as well as gem-set jewellery, showing that not only can these rare gemstones be used in various settings, but also that they are available today . . . The information supplied on each stone is comprehensive . . . Whether a newcomer to the world of gemmology or an experienced collector, this volume has something for everyone and is highly recommended."

Gems & Jewellery, published by the Gemmological Association of Great Britain

137 pages, 482 photos, 6" by 9", ISBN 978-0929975-46-7, US$19.95

Jewelry Handbook
How to Select, Wear & Care for Jewelry

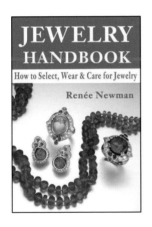

The *Jewelry Handbook* is like a Jewelry 101 course on the fundamentals of jewelry metals, settings, finishes, necklaces, chains, clasps, bracelets, rings, earrings, brooches, pins, clips, manufacturing methods and jewelry selection and care. It outlines the benefits and drawbacks of the various setting styles, mountings, chains, and metals such as gold, silver, platinum, palladium, titanium, stainless steel and tungsten. It also provides info and color photos on gemstones and fineness marks and helps you select versatile, durable jewelry that flatters your features.

"**A great introduction to jewellery** and should be required reading for all in the industry." Jack Ogden, Former CEO Gem-A (British Gemmological Association)

"**A user-friendly, beautifully illustrated guide,** allowing for quick reference to specific topics." *The Jewelry Appraiser*

"**Valuable advice for consumers and the trade**, specifically those in retail sales and perhaps even more for jewelry appraisers . . . An easy read and easy to find valuable lists and details." Richard Drucker GG, *Gem Market News*

177 pages, 297 color & 47 b/w photos, 6" x 9", ISBN 978-0-929975-38-2, US$19.95

For more information, see **www.reneenewman.com**

Other Books by RENÉE NEWMAN

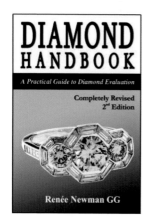

Diamond Handbook
A Practical Guide to Diamond Evaluation

Updates professionals on new developments in the diamond industry and provides advanced information on diamond grading, treatments, synthetic diamonds, fluorescence, and fancy colored diamonds. It also covers diamond grading reports, light performance, branded diamonds, diamond recutting, and antique diamond cuts and jewelry.

"**Impressively comprehensive.** . . . a **practical, well-organized and concisely written** volume, packed with valuable information. The *Diamond Handbook* is destined to become an indispensable reference for the consumer and trade professional alike." *Canadian Gemmologist*

"The text covers everything the buyer needs to know, with useful comments on lighting and first-class images. No other text in current circulation discusses recutting and its possible effects . . . **This is a must for anyone buying, testing or valuing a polished diamond and for students in many fields**." *Journal of Gemmology*

186 pages, 320 photos (most in color), 6" x 9", ISBN 978-0-929975-39-9, US$19.95

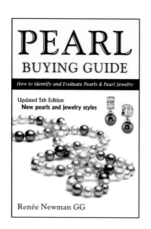

Pearl Buying Guide
How to Evaluate, Identify, Select and Care for Pearls & Pearl Jewelry

"**Copious color photographs** . . . explains how to appraise and distinguish among all varieties of pearls . . . takes potential buyers and collectors through the ins and outs of the pearl world." *Publisher's Weekly*

"**An indispensable guide** to judging [pearl] characteristics, distinguishing genuine from imitation, and making wise choices . . . useful to all types of readers, from the professional jeweler to the average patron . . . **highly recommended**." *Library Journal*

"A **well written, beautifully illustrated** book designed to help retail customers, jewelry designers, and store buyers make informed buying decisions about the various types of pearls and pearl jewelry." *Gems & Gemology*

"With loads of photos to illustrate her points, Newman tells readers how to check a pearl's luster, nacre, color, and **flaws…a gem-dandy guide to picking right-price pearls**." *Boston Herald*

154 pages, 321 photos, 6" by 9", ISBN 978-0929975-44-3, US$19.95

For more information, see **www.reneenewman.com**

Gem & Jewelry Pocket Guide

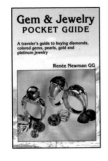

Small enough to use while shopping locally or abroad

"**Brilliantly planned, painstakingly researched, and beautifully produced** . . . this handy little book comes closer to covering all of the important bases than any similar guides have managed to do. From good descriptions of the most popular gem materials (plus gold and platinum), to jewelry craftsmanship, treatments, gem sources, appraisals, documentation, and even information about U.S. customs for foreign travelers—it is all here. I heartily endorse this wonderful pocket guide."
John S. White, former Curator of Gems & Minerals at the Smithsonian, *Lapidary Journal*

"**Short guides don't come better than this**. . . . As always with this author, the presentation is immaculate and each opening displays high-class pictures of gemstones and jewellery." *Journal of Gemmology*

154 pages, 108 color photos, 4½" by 7", ISBN 978-0929975-30-6, US$11.95
E-book version ISBN 978-0929975-49-8, US$4.99

Osteoporosis Prevention

" . . . **a complete, practical, and easy-to-read reference for osteoporosis prevention** . . . As the founding president of the Taiwan Osteoporosis Association, I am delighted to recommend this book to you."
Dr. Ko-En Huang, Founding President of TOA

"The author, Renée Newman has abundant experience in translating technical terms into everyday English. She writes this book about osteoporosis prevention from a patient's perspective. These two elements contribute to **an easy-to-read and understandable book for the public. To the medical professions, this is also a very valuable reference**."
Dr. Chyi-Her Lin, Dean of Medical College, Natl Cheng Kung Univ / Taiwan

"I was impressed with the comprehensive nature of *Osteoporosis Prevention* and its use of scientific sources. . . . Another good feature is that the book has informative illustrations and tables, which help clarify important points. I congratulate the author for writing **a sound and thorough guide to osteoporosis prevention**." Ronald Lawrence MD, PhD
Co-chair of the first Symposium on Osteoporosis of the National Institute on Aging

"The book is written from a patient's experience and her secrets to bone care. This book is **so interesting that I finished reading it the following day** . . . The author translates all the technical terms into everyday English which makes this book so easy to read and understand." Dr. Sheng-Mou Hou, Ex-minister, Dept. of Health / Taiwan

You can get free information about osteoporosis prevention, bone density testing and reports at: **www.avoidboneloss.com**

176 pages, 6" X 9", ISBN 978-0929975-37-5, US$15.95

Order Form

TITLE	Price	Quantity	Total
Gemstone Buying Guide	$19.95		
Exotic Gems, Volume 4	$19.95		
Exotic Gems, Volume 3	$19.95		
Exotic Gems, Volume 2	$19.95		
Exotic Gems, Volume 1	$19.95		
Gold, Platinum, Silver, Palladium & Other . . .	$19.95		
Rare Gemstones	$19.95		
Diamond Handbook	$19.95		
Pearl Buying Guide	$19.95		
Jewelry Handbook	$19.95		
Gem & Jewelry Pocket Guide	$11.95		
Osteoporosis Prevention	$15.95		
		Book Total	
SALES TAX for California residents only		**(book total x $.09)**	
SHIPPING: USA: first book $5.00, each additional copy $2.00 Canada & Mexico - airmail: first book $25.00, each addl. $5.00 All other foreign countries - airmail: first book $35.00, each addl. $5.00			
TOTAL AMOUNT with tax (if applicable) and shipping (Pay foreign orders with an international money order or a check drawn on a U.S. bank.)		**TOTAL**	

Available at major book stores or by mail. For quantity orders e-mail: intljpubl@aol.com.

Mail check or money order in U.S. funds

To: International Jewelry Publications
P.O. Box 13384, Los Angeles, CA 90013-0384 USA

Ship to:

Name_____

Address_____

City_____ State or Province_____

Postal or Zip Code_____ Country_____